INTERNATIONAL SERIES OF MONOGRAPHS ON

PURE AND APPLIED MATHEMATICS

General Editors: I. N. Sneddon, M. Stark and S. Ulam

Volume 33

AN INTRODUCTION TO PROJECTIVE GEOMETRY

An Introduction
to
Projective Geometry

by

DANIEL PEDOE

Professor of Mathematics,
Purdue University,
Lafayette, Indiana

A Pergamon Press Book

THE MACMILLAN COMPANY
NEW YORK
1963

THE MACMILLAN COMPANY
60 Fifth Avenue
New York 11, N.Y.

This book is distributed by
THE MACMILLAN COMPANY · NEW YORK
pursuant to a special arrangement with
PERGAMON PRESS LIMITED
Oxford, England

Library of Congress Catalog Card No. 62-22053

Set in Modern No. 7, 10 on 12 pt. and printed in Great Britain by
John Wright & Sons Ltd. at the Stonebridge Press, Bristol

To my wife

CONTENTS

VII. HOMOGENEOUS COORDINATES AND COLLINEATIONS

VIII. CROSS-RATIOS

IX. CONICS

X. PROJECTIVE SPACE OF n DIMENSIONS

APPENDIX

PREFACE

MATHEMATICAL development, as knowledge advances, always tends to outflank the carefully prepared positions taken up by the writers of textbooks. This, of course, shows that mathematics is a living subject, but also explains the appearance of the present volume, which is designed to introduce the honours (or beginning graduate) student to some of the new developments of the past thirty years, so that he will be able to read research papers on projective geometry, and perhaps make his own contribution to the subject.

But enough of classical projective geometry is given to form a suitable introductory text for beginners as well, so that this book can be used by students of all grades.

In any case, the classical concepts cannot be disregarded in any treatment of modern projective geometry, since they are the inspiration of much recent work. The work of Marshall Hall, Jnr. [8]† and Reinhold Baer [2] has thrown new light on concepts such as the plane perspectivity transformation. To give the background to these discoveries, the first chapter develops the theoretical and practical geometry of perspectivity transformations. The modern theoretical developments will be found in Chapters V and VI.

Most of this book is restricted to the projective geometry of the plane, since there is quite enough to study there before we reach up into space, but the last chapter discusses the incidence properties of projective space of n dimensions, in a reasonable amount of detail.

A summary of the algebraic results assumed in the text is given in an Appendix. Now that courses in Modern Algebra are a part of every university curriculum, the need to insert chapters on algebra in books on geometry is not as pressing as it was some years ago.

Rigour in mathematics is, of course, a *sine qua non*. It should interest those who may be disposed to believe that all outstanding problems in classical projective geometry have been solved to note that Pickert, in his *Projektive Ebenen* (Berlin, 1955), lists eight

† The references are to the Bibliography.

defective versions of the classical Hessenberg theorem, that *the assumption of the Pappus theorem involves the truth of the Desargues theorem*. Two of these defective proofs are by Hessenberg himself. We ourselves do not escape calumny, but we have noted that the Pickert list can be extended! Hilbert in his *Grundlagen der Geometrie* (Leipzig, 1930, p. 111) evades the issue most skilfully.

We should be more than human were we not to confess to a slight lightening of the spirit on discovering that Arno Cronheim's excellent proof [7] of the Hessenberg theorem omits one special case, which, fortunately, does not affect the final result. Full details are given in Chapter II.

Although this book aims at complete rigour, we have also tried to write a rounded and (we trust) readable book which may give the reader some of the pleasure we have had in writing it.

Of course, we owe much to those writers who have preceded us. Professor Marshall Hall, Jnr., and the publishers of his *The Theory of Groups* (New York, 1959) have generously given us permission to use Chapter 20 of that excellent work, in which Professor Hall's publications, extending the work of Ruth Moufang, are summarized. The book by Pickert already mentioned has been invaluable, and we owe much to Professor Reinhold Baer's papers [2], and were stimulated by his *Linear Algebra and Projective Geometry* (New York, 1952). Our debt to Professor B. Segre's *Lezioni di Geometria Moderna* (Bologna, 1948) and to Professor E. Artin's *Geometric Algebra* (New York, 1957) is also very clear. It was with great reluctance that we omitted Artin's attractive method for introducing coordinates, but Hall's approach seems to be the more natural one, and a choice had to be made.

Finally, we owe much to our former collaboration with Sir William Hodge; and the late Professor H. F. Baker's *Principles of Geometry*, especially Vol. II (Cambridge, 1922), is a veritable treasure-house for the patient reader.

Much, of course, has been omitted in this book. We do not, for example, discuss the notion of *order* in a projective plane. But the reader is probably already acquainted with Professor H. S. M. Coxeter's *The Real Projective Plane* (Cambridge, 1955) where this, and other matters, are very adequately dealt with. We have been motivated throughout by the desire to keep this book a reasonable size, so that the appetite of the willing reader may be stimulated, rather than sated, by what he will find herein.

As an introduction to projective geometry, for a two hours a week course lasting approximately 28 weeks, the following is suggested:

Chapter I, Chapter II (omitting §§ 9–13), Chapter III (explaining the results, but omitting the proofs in §§ 6–7, 9–13 and 17–19), Chapter IV, Chapter V (omitting § 21), and Chapters IX and X.

Chapter VIII can be added if there is time, but in an introductory course, cross-ratios over a commutative field should be discussed first.

Such a course has proved successful in Singapore, with students selected for Honours after taking a general degree.

Similar courses, but for three hours a week, and lasting a semester, have also been given at Purdue University in the Junior year. Most American students reach University with comparatively little training in geometry, but once interest in projective geometry has been aroused, and this can be done by the perspective drawing recommended in Chapter I, the valuable results of a course similar to the one we have indicated are soon manifest.

This book was begun in Khartoum, Sudan, and completed in Singapore, but any defects, and the author is only too conscious of them, cannot entirely be attributed to the exigencies of the respective climates of these fascinating places. In Singapore I was greatly indebted for his accurate typing to my secretary, Mr. Harry Song, and I wish to thank him and the many others, unknown to me, whose skill has gone into the production of this book. In Lafayette Miss Geraldine Jensen, of Purdue University, has given valuable help with the final reading of proofs and the preparation of the index.

Finally, a word about the system of references. Theorems are printed in italics and numbered afresh from the beginning of each chapter. References to theorems give the section and chapter in which they occur, the chapter number being omitted if the theorem is in the same chapter.

D. P.

Lafayette, Ind.

Nov. 1962

CHAPTER I

INTRODUCTION
TO THE SUBJECT MATTER

1. Historical

It is thought that geometry first developed as a physical science in those Middle Eastern countries where the annual flooding of fields by a river obliterates the boundary-marks between plots of land.

This is a plausible hypothesis. But anyone who has lived on the banks of the Nile, say, knows that very simple measurements are sufficient to re-establish boundary-marks, and that little theory need be involved. It has been known for many centuries, for example, that a triangle with sides of 3, 4 and 5 units is a right-angled triangle. But the advance in knowledge from this simple fact to the statement and the proof of Pythagoras' theorem, that the square on the hypotenuse of a right-angled triangle is equal to the sum of the squares on the other two sides—such an advance is one of the greatest in the history of human thought. Very little, unfortunately, is known about the first stumbling steps which must have been taken before this tremendous leap took place.

The theory that all such advances are dictated by economic necessity does not help us here, since the ancient Greeks, who developed geometry to the polished form in which it is found in Euclid, were little interested in practical applications of the results of their speculations. On the other hand, we do know that logical thought fascinated them.

In fact, the Greeks laid the foundations for logic as we know it today. They realized that in developing a system of mathematics not everything can be *proved*, that some assertions must be accepted as being *given* before mathematics of any kind can be attempted. We shall not, of course, depart from this fundamental method of developing a rigorous mathematical theory, but in this first chapter we shall not emphasize rigour, our aim being to introduce concepts which will explain the motivation of subsequent chapters.

2. Conical projection

We shall assume a knowledge of elementary geometry, and begin by showing how *conical projection* can illuminate plane geometry, and lead to the ideas of *projective geometry*.

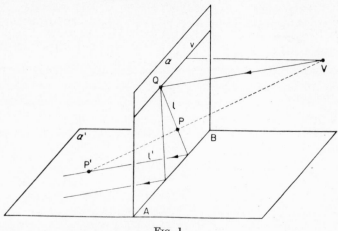

Fig. 1

We imagine two planes α and α' which intersect in a line AB. If the plane α is assumed to be transparent, and has points and lines marked on it, as if it were a lantern-slide, a point-source of light at V will project a picture of the points and lines in the plane α on to the plane α'.

A point P in α is projected into a point P' in α', and it is clear that a line l in α is projected into a line l' in α'.

Again, the intersection of two lines l and m in α is projected into the intersection of the two projected lines l' and m' in α'. Every line in the plane α is projected into a line in the plane α', and every line l' in the plane α' arises from a line l in the plane α. But there is an important exception to this rule.

Through V draw a plane parallel to the plane α'. This plane will intersect the plane α in a line v. This line v is called the *vanishing line*. No point on v projects into an ordinary point in α', since if P is on v, the line VP is *parallel* to the plane α', and does not meet it.

We notice that all lines in the plane α' which are parallel to a given line l' arise from the lines in the plane α which pass through a fixed point on the vanishing line v, and this fixed point is uniquely determined by the *direction* of l'.

In fact, the join of V to a line in α' determines a plane which intersects the line v in a point Q which is such that VQ is parallel to the line in the plane α'. Hence a set or family of lines in the plane α' which are all in the same direction determine a unique point Q on the vanishing line v. Lines in the plane α which pass through Q project into lines in the plane α' which are all parallel to the line VQ.

3. Perspective

Before we discuss the extension in mathematical thought which arose from this simple geometrical figure, let us see how painting was influenced by it. A study of early painting in any National Gallery will show that little was known of *perspective*, the art of making a two-dimensional picture look three-dimensional, before the fifteenth century.

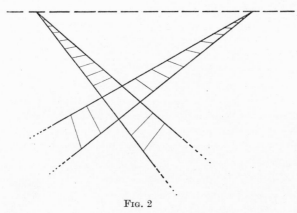

FIG. 2

Some early painters were very interested in the theory of perspective, and wrote treatises on the subject. We need only cite Albrecht Dürer, who published *Messung mit dem Richtscheid* in 1525, a book which contains much information on the mathematics of drawing. Dürer illustrated his knowledge in his work, of course.

The geometrical construction above gives us an adequate theory if we imagine that a scene is being viewed by one eye, the vertex V of projection, and projected on to a plane. The scene can be thought of as the plane α', and the canvas as the plane α. All lines in α' which are parallel are made to meet in α on a line, the vanishing line, and different directions in α correspond to different points on the vanishing line.

Thus, to represent two sets of railway lines going in different directions, we need only draw them as in the diagram on p. 3.

But it must be emphasized that this theory of perspective is only an approximate theory, since most of us view the external world through two eyes, not one, and also possess stereoscopic vision. Modern painters are aware of this, and many modern paintings do not subscribe to the classical theory of perspective.

4. Conic sections

Returning to our projections from the point V: rays passing through V form a *conical surface*, and the process of projecting from V is called *conical projection*. We notice that points on the line AB, the line of intersection of the planes α and α', are unaltered by projection, since the line (or ray) joining V to a point P on AB which is considered to be in α meets α' in the same point P.

Hence any line in α which meets AB in a point P is projected into a line α' which meets AB in the same point P. In other words: *a line and its projection intersect on AB*, which is called the *axis of projection*.

So far we have only talked of points and lines and their projections. What happens if we have a circle in the plane α, and join all its points to V? We obtain a *cone*, and the section of this cone by the plane α' is the projection of the circle. The reader will not expect this section always to be a circle.

We shall show, by actual drawing, that the sections can be either an ellipse, a parabola or a hyperbola. In fact, the sections are the *conic sections*, which were studied by the ancient Greeks as the curves derived by taking sections of a right circular cone. Our cone is only right circular if V happens to be on the perpendicular to the plane α which passes through the centre of the circle in α. But the sections are of the same kind.

If the reader has a reading-lamp with a simple non-fluted shade, he can easily obtain the conic sections by observing the shadows cast on a wall. If the top rim of the shade is circular, the light coming from the top of the lamp forms a right circular cone of rays, and by tilting the lamp, the conic sections may be observed.

Beginning with a circle, when the top of the lamp is pointed directly at the wall, tilting will produce an oval, or ellipse, and further tilting will produce a parabola, and then both branches of a hyperbola. These curves will be discussed more fully below. Their production as shadows is very satisfying to the aesthetic sense, often very well developed in mathematicians. During the last war, for some sinister reason, the only lamp-shades obtainable in England were all fluted. A stirring letter from a Cambridge mathematician appeared in the London *Times*, pleading for lamp-shades of the old simple type, and asking where he could buy a lamp-shade which was a simple frustum of a right circular cone!

5. Ideal elements

We return to our two planes, α and α', and the vertex V of projection. We have seen that every point in the plane α is projected into a point in the plane α', and that every line in the plane α is projected into a line in the plane α'. But we have not seen this at all! There are exceptions! Points on the vanishing line v in α do not appear at all in α'. Lines which meet in a point of v project into parallel lines in α'. The line v in α has no image in the plane α'.

If we insist that every point in α must give rise to a point in α', and every line in α to a line in α', we must introduce new points, called *ideal points*, into the plane α'. We can then say that a set of parallel lines in α' all pass through an *ideal point at infinity*; that different directions give different ideal points, and that all ideal points lie on an *ideal line*, the *line at infinity*. This is the line which is to correspond to v, the vanishing line.

6. Projective geometry

In ordinary Euclidean geometry we do not consider ideal points or lines. If we do so, we are extending the geometry. When we drop the adjective *ideal*, and consider *all* points and lines in a plane, with no class-distinction between one point and another point, or one line and another line, we no longer have Euclidean geometry, but a new and more comprehensive geometry, called *projective geometry*.

In projective geometry the emphasis is on the two concepts *point* and *line*, with a relation between them, the relation of *incidence*. A given line may, or may not, contain a given point. If it does, we say that the line *passes through* or *contains* the given point, and we say that the given point *lies on* or is *contained in* the given line. The fundamental relations assumed in projective geometry are extremely simple. They are:

Two *points* determine a *line*, on which they both lie;

Two *lines* determine a *point*, through which they both pass.

These relations are always assumed to be true, so that the concept of lines being parallel does not enter into projective geometry. Two distinct lines always meet in a point.

7. Principle of duality

We observe a remarkable similarity of pattern between the two sentences which express the fundamental properties of lines and points. It is only *language* which prevents our changing one sentence into the other by the automatic process of substituting "point" for "line", and "line" for "point". We also have to interchange "lie" and "pass", and "on" and "through".

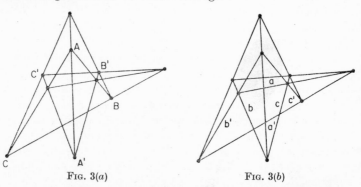

FIG. 3(*a*)   FIG. 3(*b*)

We say that the entities *point* and *line* are *dual* concepts. It is a remarkable fact, expressed in *the Principle of Duality*, that from any true theorem in projective geometry we can obtain another true theorem by an automatic interchange of "point" and "line", with consequential linguistic changes described above. We elaborate our statement.

A theorem in projective geometry is one which only involves points, lines and incidence properties. Such a theorem will retain its meaning after being submitted to conical projection. The notions of distance, angle, ratio, direction, etc., do not enter into projective geometry, but can be brought in at a later stage.

8. Desargues' theorem

We consider such a theorem, the celebrated and fundamental *Theorem of Desargues* (see Figs. 3(*a*), 3(*b*)).

1. *If two triangles ABC and A'B'C' are such that the lines AA', BB' and CC' all pass through one point, then the intersections of the*

sides BC and B'C', CA and C'A', and AB and A'B' give three points which lie on a line.

If we assume this theorem, the dual theorem is:

2. *If two triangles abc and a'b'c' are such that the points aa', bb' and cc' all lie on a line, then the joins of the vertices bc and b'c', ca and c'a', and ab and a'b' give three lines which pass through one point.*

Our notation is self-evident. We call the line joining the points P and Q *the line PQ*, and the point of intersection of the lines p and q is called *the point pq*. The Desargues theorem is one which we shall examine at a later stage (Ch. II). We shall then see that the dual theorem can be proved if we assume the original theorem. But we shall soon make use of the dual theorem.

9. Two constructions

Before we do this, a word about the possibilities of projective geometry will not be out of place. It may be thought that very little can be done with mere points, lines and incidence properties. Projective geometry is the geometry of the unmarked ruler. Let us give some examples of what can be done with such an instrument!

Two lines l and m are drawn on a sheet of paper, but intersect at a point which is off the sheet (see Fig. 4). Draw through a point P, which is marked on the sheet, a line which will pass through the inaccessible intersection of l and m.

A solution involving only accessible points is obtained by using a Desargues configuration in which the perspective triangles ABC and $A'B'C'$ are such that A and B lie on l, A' and B' lie on m, and P, the given point, is the intersection of AC and $A'C'$. Figure 4 makes this clear. If the point P' is the intersection of BC and $B'C'$, then Desargues' theorem says that P, P' and the intersection of AB and $A'B'$, which is the intersection of l and m, are collinear. Hence by joining P to P', we have a line through the inaccessible intersection of l and m.

Using only a straight edge, we may even plot as many points as we please on a conic section. The construction goes back to the seventeenth century, and may be stated as a theorem, or *Maclaurin's construction of a conic*:

3. *ABC is a variable triangle which is such that the vertices B and C respectively move on two fixed lines l and m, and each side BC, CA and AB of the triangle passes through a fixed point.*† *Then the vertex A describes a conic section.*

† The three points must not be collinear. See Ch. II, § 4, Ex. 3.

The construction of such a triangle is very simple, and the theorem will impress far more if a number of points are actually plotted.

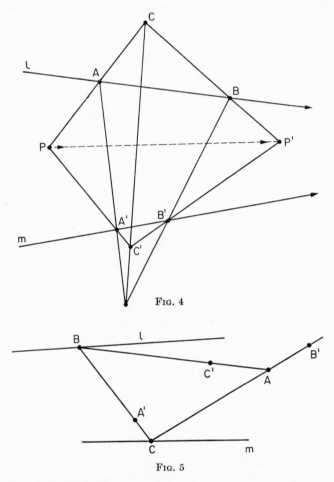

FIG. 4

FIG. 5

We start off with the given lines l and m, and the fixed points A', B' and C' through which the sides BC, CA and AB are to pass. The point B can be taken anywhere on l. We then join BA' to meet m in C. The intersection of CB' and BC' gives A. Varying B gives different positions of A, and it will be seen that the locus described by A is indeed a conic section. This will be proved later (Ch. IX, § 6).

Of course, without a great deal more thought we shall not know what kind of a conic section this construction will give us. But we now show how our three-dimensional conical projections can be realized in a plane. Our only mathematical instruments will be a straight edge and a parallel ruler, and we shall be able to produce the three types of conic section at will.

Exercises

1. The lines a and a', and the lines b and b' are drawn on a sheet of paper, and both intersections, that of a and a' and of b and b', are inaccessible. Show that two applications of the Desargues theorem will give a line on the sheet which passes through both inaccessible points, if this line does, in fact, traverse the sheet. (It is assumed that the intersections of a and b, and of a' and b' respectively lie on the sheet.)

2. The same lines are given as in the first exercise, but c is a line drawn on the paper. Show how to draw a line which passes through the intersection of c and the line joining the two inaccessible points given by a and a', b and b'. (The vertices of the triangle formed by a, b and c are assumed to lie on the sheet, as well as the intersection of a' and b'.)

10. Plane perspective

Returning to the planes α and α' (Fig. 1), we suppose that a figure in the plane α has been projected from the vertex V into a figure in the plane α'. We now ignore the vertex V, and keeping the plane α' fixed in position, we rotate the plane α about the axis of intersection AB until the planes α and α' coincide. This process is called *rabatment*.

We now have two figures in one plane. To every point P of the one figure there corresponds a unique point P' of the other figure, and conversely, and to every line l of the first figure there corresponds a unique line l' of the second figure, and conversely. Any two corresponding lines l and l' meet on a fixed line, the axis of intersection.

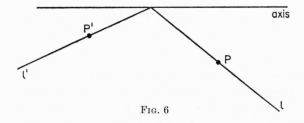

Fig. 6

From the given data, and using the dual of Desargues' theorem given above, it now follows that the joins PP' of corresponding pairs of points all pass through a fixed point in the plane, which we shall call V.†

To prove this we merely take three lines l, m and n, forming a triangle PQR, and the three corresponding lines l', m' and n', forming a triangle $P'Q'R'$. We know that l meets l', that m meets m', and that n meets n' on the axis of intersection. Hence, by the dual Desargues' theorem, the lines PP', QQ' and RR' all pass through one

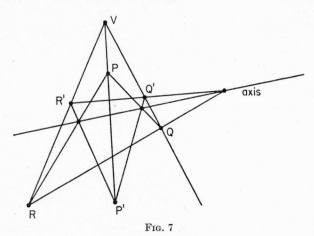

Fig. 7

point. Since Q and Q', R and R' can be regarded as fixed, we see that PP' always passes through a fixed point, the intersection of QQ' and RR'.

Our original conical projection, after rabatment, has now given us a transformation of the plane which is called *plane perspective*. This transformation of the plane is defined if we are given:

(1) the vertex V of perspective;

(2) the axis of intersection, which we now call the *axis of perspective*;

(3) one pair P, P' of corresponding points.

To prove this, all that we have to do is to find the point Q' which corresponds to a given point Q.

Now we know that VQ passes through Q' (in technical language V, Q and Q' are *collinear*), and we also know that the line $P'Q'$ corresponds to the line PQ, and that these two lines therefore intersect on the

† We can prove this theorem without invoking Desargues (Ch. V, § 14, Th. 18).

axis of perspective. Hence, to find Q', all that we need to do is to join PQ, which meets the axis of perspective in R, say, and then find where RP' meets VQ. This gives the point Q'.

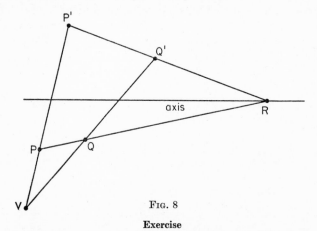

FIG. 8

Exercise

1. The points of α are projected from two distinct vertices V and V' on to α'. If the projection of P from V is P', and that of P from V' is P'', show that the lines $P'P''$ in α' always pass through a fixed point. Using the Desargues theorem, deduce that the transformation of the plane α' given by $P' \rightarrow P''$ is a plane perspective.

11. The vanishing line

In the original conical projection there was a vanishing line in the plane α, and points on it were projected into points at infinity in the plane α'. We know that this vanishing line is parallel to the axis of

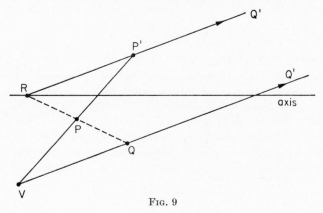

FIG. 9

perspective, which was formerly the axis of intersection. Hence, in order to determine the vanishing line, we need only one point on it. We must therefore determine Q when Q' is at infinity. We draw any line through V, and assuming that Q' is at infinity on this line, we find Q. The construction above shows that we must determine the point R in which $P'Q'$ meets the axis of perspective. Since $P'Q'$ is now parallel to the line VQ, which is given, R is determined. The point Q is then the intersection of RP and the line VQ.

It is not difficult to show that as we vary the *line* VQ the points Q we construct move on a line parallel to the axis of perspective. In fact, triangles PQV and PRP' are similar, so that

$$PQ/PR = PV/PP' = \text{constant},$$

and therefore, since R moves on a line, Q moves on a parallel line.

But all we need is the possibility, which we have demonstrated, of *constructing* the vanishing line in a plane perspective determined by the vertex, the axis of perspective and one pair of corresponding points P, P'.

Finally, we note that when Q is on the vanishing line, any line through Q is transformed into a line *parallel to* VQ, since Q' is at infinity on VQ. We shall make use of this fact in the following examples.

12. Quadrangle into parallelogram

We begin by showing that any quadrangle $ABCD$ can be projected, by a suitable conical projection, into a parallelogram $A'B'C'D'$.

We demonstrate the existence of the corresponding plane perspective.

Let the opposite sides AB and CD of the quadrangle meet in E, and let the sides CB and DA meet in F. Then we set up a plane perspective in which EF is the *vanishing line*. When this is done, the transformed quadrangle $A'B'C'D'$ will be such that $A'B'$ meets $C'D'$ at infinity ($A'B'$ is parallel to $C'D'$), and $C'B'$ meets $A'D'$ at infinity ($C'B'$ is parallel to $A'D'$).

We may choose V, the vertex of perspective, at any suitable point, and since the assignment of V, the vertex of perspective, the axis of perspective and a pair of corresponding points determines the vanishing line, we expect that the assignment of V, the vanishing line and a pair of corresponding points will determine the axis of perspective. But there is no need to prove this, since we can construct the parallelogram $A'B'C'D'$ immediately once we have chosen V, and the point on VA, say, which is to be A'.

Then $A'D'$ is a line through A' parallel to VF, and D' is the intersection of VD with $A'D'$. The line $A'B'$ passes through A' and is parallel to VE, and B' is the intersection of VB with $A'B'$. The line $D'C'$ passes through D' and is parallel to VE, and C' is the intersection of VC with $D'C'$.

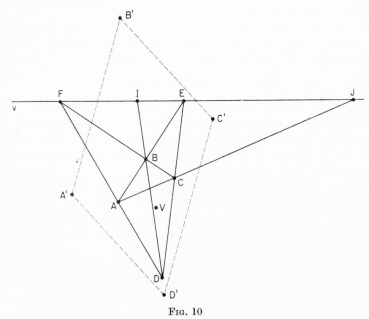

FIG. 10

We have therefore constructed the four points A', B', C', D', and a test of the accuracy of our drawing is to verify that $B'C'$ is parallel to $A'D'$. We may also verify that the lines in the original figure and the transformed lines intersect on a line, the axis of perspective.

13. Quadrangle into square

We now go a step farther, and show that a quadrangle $ABCD$ can be projected into a *square*. We first require the parallelogram constructed above to become a rectangle, and then demand that the angle between the diagonals of the rectangle be a right angle also. If these conditions are satisfied, the rectangle is necessarily a square.

If the vertex of perspective, V, is chosen so that the points E and F subtend a right angle at V, then the angle between $A'D'$ and $D'C'$

will be a right angle, since $A'D'$ is parallel to VF, and $D'C'$ is parallel to VE. The parallelogram is then a rectangle. Let DB meet EF at I, and let CA meet EF at J. If the angle between VI and VJ is a right angle, the angle between $D'B'$ and $C'A'$ will be a right angle, and the rectangle is a square (see Fig. 11).

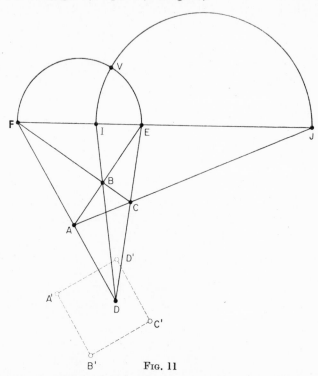

Fig. 11

Hence, to project a quadrangle into a square, V must be chosen so that EF and IJ both subtend right angles at V. The angle in a semicircle is a right angle, so that all we do is to find V as one of the two points of intersection of a circle on EF as diameter and a circle on IJ as diameter.

With EF as vanishing line, the previous construction now transforms the quadrangle $ABCD$ into a square $A'B'C'D'$.

14. Conics

We now come to the conical projection of a circle. Plane perspective enables us to draw for ourselves the curves obtained by three-dimensional projection and section. We begin with a circle $\mathscr{C}$, a vertex of perspective V, and a vanishing line v. We take any suitable point P on the circle, and assign the point P' which is to correspond to it on VP. If Q is any other point on the circle, and PQ meets v in R, then $P'Q'$ must be parallel to VR. Since Q' is also on

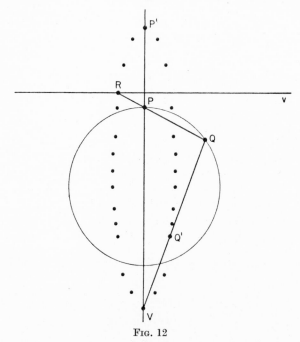

Fig. 12

VQ, the point Q' is easily constructed as the intersection of VQ and a line through P' parallel to VR. Hence an adequate number of points on the projection of $\mathscr{C}$ can be constructed.

It is clear that the projection of a circle depends in a fundamental way on the relation of the circle to the vanishing line v.

If the circle does not cut v, there are no points at infinity on the transformed curve, which will be an oval, contained in some finite part of the plane. This curve is an *ellipse* (Fig. 12).

If the circle cuts v in two points, I and J, say (see Fig. 13), there will be two points at infinity in the directions VI and VJ. The *tangents* to the circle at I and J transform into lines which are parallel to VI and to VJ respectively, but do not intersect the transformed curve in any finite point; whereas the general line parallel to VI or to VJ arises from a general line through I or through J, and since such a line cuts the circle in another point besides I or J, the general line parallel to VI or to VJ does cut the transformed curve in one finite point.

The two special lines which do not meet the transformed curve in any finite point are called *asymptotes*. The curve itself is the *hyperbola*. It has two distinct parts, or *branches*, the one arising

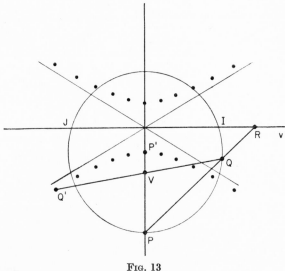

FIG. 13

from a part of the circle which can be traversed continuously in moving from I to J, and the other from the other part of the circle which can be traversed continuously in moving from I to J.

The case which may be considered as intermediate to the two above is that in which the circle *touches* the vanishing line (Fig. 14). The transformed curve is all in one piece, and there is a certain direction in its plane which is such that any line in the plane in this direction meets the transformed curve in one finite point and a point at infinity. These parallel lines are the transforms of those passing through the point of contact of the circle and the vanishing line v. The only line which meets the transformed curve, the *parabola*, in *two* points at infinity is the transform of v, and this is the line at infinity. Hence there should be no confusion between the parabola and one branch of a hyperbola, since the parabola has no asymptotes.

It is clear that a detailed study of the conic sections can be made, using the above approach, and such studies can be found in various textbooks. Our aim in this chapter is merely to introduce the conic sections via plane perspective, and perhaps to persuade the reader to carry out some of the constructions we have described above.

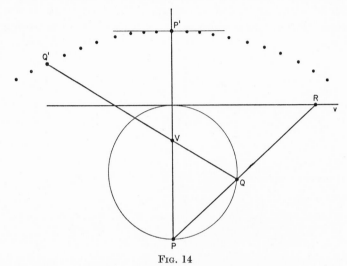

FIG. 14

We conclude the chapter with a description of two special types of plane perspective, which will be used in subsequent chapters.

15. Dilatations and translations

As we have seen, a plane perspective is a one-to-one mapping of a plane onto itself which maps lines on lines, and is defined if the vertex of perspective, the axis of perspective and a pair of corresponding points are given. If the axis of perspective is the line at infinity, the perspective is called a *dilatation*, and we have the situation shown in Fig. 15.

The joins of corresponding points P, P' all pass through a fixed point V, and corresponding lines are parallel. This mapping is determined if V and a pair of corresponding points P, P' are given. Metrically, we see that the segment PQ is *dilated* into the parallel segment $P'Q'$, and that $P'Q'/PQ = VP'/VP$, which is a constant ratio.

If the vertex V is also at infinity, the mapping is called a *translation*.† It is determined when a pair of corresponding points

† When the vertex V lies on the axis of perspective, the mapping is called an *elation* (see Ch. V, § 15). A translation is an elation with axis at infinity.

P, P' are given. If Q, Q' is another pair of corresponding points, we see that PP' is parallel to QQ', and PQ is parallel to $P'Q'$, corresponding to the respective vertex and axis of perspective being at infinity. Metrically, the segment PQ is translated through the fixed distance PP' to the position $P'Q'$.

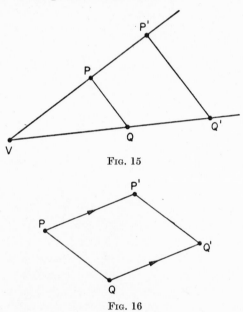

FIG. 15

FIG. 16

It is useful to consider the consequences of carrying out a sequence of transformations in a plane, of the type we have been considering. A dilatation with vertex V will be denoted by σ, so that $\sigma(P) = P'$ expresses the fact that the effect of σ on P is to produce P'.

We may also write this as

$$P = \sigma^{-1}(P'),$$

which defines the inverse of the dilatation σ. This is also a dilatation, vertex V. Naturally we have

$$\sigma\sigma^{-1}(P') = \sigma(P) = P',$$

which shows that the transformation $\sigma\sigma^{-1}$ is the *identity* transformation, which leaves P' unchanged. We write this special, but fundamental, transformation as 1, so that $\sigma\sigma^{-1} = 1$. Similarly $\sigma^{-1}\sigma = 1$.

We can prove that the product of any two dilatations σ, σ' is again a dilatation. Let σ have vertex V, and σ' vertex V', and let $\sigma(P) = P'$, and $\sigma'(P') = P''$. Suppose that the line PP'' meets VV' at V'' (see Fig. 17).

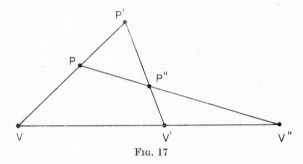

FIG. 17

Since, using elementary geometry (Menelaus' theorem),

$$\frac{VP}{PP'} \cdot \frac{P'P''}{P''V'} \cdot \frac{V'V''}{V''V} = -1,$$

V'' is a fixed point. Again, $\sigma(P) = P'$, $\sigma'(P') = P'' = \sigma'\sigma(P)$, so that the product transformation $\sigma'\sigma$ acting on P produces P''. To show that $\sigma'\sigma$ is a dilatation vertex V'', we only have to show that the ratio $V''P/V''P'' = $ constant. This follows immediately on applying Menelaus' theorem to the triangle $PP'P''$.

If V'' is at infinity, $\sigma'\sigma$ is a translation, which is, of course, a special case of a dilatation. Anticipating later definitions (with which the reader is probably already familiar) (see Appendix) we say:

4. *The dilatations in a plane form a group of transformations of the plane.*

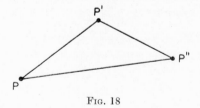

FIG. 18

It should probably be stressed once more at this point that in this chapter we are merely producing results which will supply the motivation for the abstract reasoning of later chapters (Ch. V, §15).

3

A translation τ is given if the image P' of one point P is given, so that $\tau(P) = P'$. If τ' be another translation, and $\tau'(P') = P''$, then $\tau'\tau(P) = \tau'(P') = P''$, and $\tau'\tau$ is a translation which maps P on P''. The proof is evident from the diagram. The segment PP' is fixed in magnitude and direction, and so is the segment $P'P''$. Hence the segment PP'' is also fixed in magnitude and direction, and represents a definite translation. It follows that:

5. *The translations of the plane also form a group of transformations.*

This group must be a subgroup of the group of dilatations. We now prove:

6. *If σ is a dilatation, and τ a translation, then $\sigma\tau\sigma^{-1}$ is a translation with the direction of τ.*

Let σ have vertex V. Then σ^{-1} also has vertex V. Suppose that $\sigma^{-1}(P) = P'$, and that $\tau(P') = Q'$. Then the segment $P'Q'$ is given in magnitude and direction.

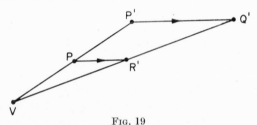

FIG. 19

If $R' = \sigma(Q')$, then since $P = \sigma(P')$ we must have PR' parallel to $P'Q'$. Therefore

$$R' = \sigma(Q') = \sigma\tau(P') = \sigma\tau\sigma^{-1}(P),$$

and since $\qquad PR'/P'Q' = VP/VP' = \text{constant},$

the segment PR' is fixed both in magnitude and direction, the direction being that of the translation τ. The theorem is therefore proved.

We have seen that a translation τ is defined when we are given $\tau(P) = P'$. Suppose that the segment PP' is c units in length. We

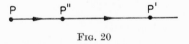

FIG. 20

now *define* the translation τ^α to have the same direction as τ, but, in a sense, to be α times as effective. More precisely, if $\tau^\alpha(P) = P''$, then P'' is to lie on the line PP', but $PP'' = c\alpha$.

We should have said what kind of a number α is supposed to be. For our purpose here α may be supposed to be a rational number.

The notation may be worrying the reader. He will soon see that there is a good reason for writing τ^α in an exponential form.

Now let τ_1, τ_2 be any two translations. We prove that

7. $$(\tau_1 \tau_2)^\alpha = (\tau_1)^\alpha (\tau_2)^\alpha.$$

Let τ_2 be represented by the directed segment PP', and let τ_1 be represented by the directed segment $P'Q'$. Then (see Fig. 21)

$$\tau_1 \tau_2(P) = \tau_1(P') = Q',$$

and $$(\tau_1 \tau_2)^\alpha (P) = R',$$

where $PR' = \alpha PQ'$, remembering, of course, that PQ' represents $\tau_1 \tau_2$. On the other hand,

$$(\tau_2)^\alpha (P) = S, \quad \text{where} \quad PS = \alpha PP',$$

so that $$(\tau_1)^\alpha (S) = R', \quad \text{since} \quad SR' = \alpha P'Q',$$

and therefore, finally,

$$(\tau_1)^\alpha (\tau_2)^\alpha (P) = R' = (\tau_1 \tau_2)^\alpha (P).$$

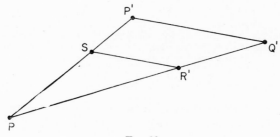

FIG. 21

This is, of course, elementary, but it does show that the mapping

$$\tau \to \tau^\alpha$$

is a *homomorphism* (see Appendix).

If $\alpha = 0$, every point P in the plane is mapped on itself, and we have the identity mapping, which we have already represented by the symbol 1. Our notation then gives the suggestive formula:

$$\tau^0 = 1.$$

If $\alpha = 1$, the translation τ is mapped on itself, and we have

$$\tau^1 = \tau.$$

The reader will have no difficulty in seeing that if $\alpha = -1$, the symbol τ^{-1} is identical with the inverse of τ, which is described by the same symbol.

Let us consider the translation represented by $\tau^\alpha \tau^\beta$. If $PQ = \beta PP'$, and $QQ' = \alpha PP'$, then (see Fig. 22)

$$\tau^\alpha . \tau^\beta(P) = \tau^\alpha(Q) = Q',$$

so that

$$PQ' = PQ + QQ' = (\alpha + \beta)\,PP',$$

and we may therefore write

$$\tau^\alpha . \tau^\beta = \tau^{\alpha+\beta}.$$

Again, $(\tau^\beta)^\alpha (P) = Q'$, where $PQ' = \alpha(PQ'')$, and $Q'' = \tau^\beta(P)$, so that $PQ'' = \beta(PQ)$, and

$$(\tau^\beta)^\alpha (P) = Q', \quad \text{where} \quad PQ' = \alpha\beta(PQ).$$

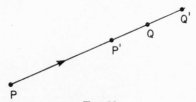

FIG. 22

We therefore have the relation

$$(\tau^\beta)^\alpha = \tau^{\alpha\beta}.$$

Our final theorem is the following:

8. *If $\alpha \neq 0$, and V is a given point, then there exists a unique dilatation σ which has V as vertex, and is such that*

$$\tau^\alpha = \sigma\tau\sigma^{-1}$$

for any translation τ.

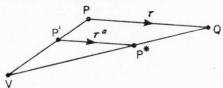

FIG. 23

We note that α is given, and is not zero. Let P be any point, and suppose that $\tau(P) = Q$. Take a point P' on VP such that $VP'/VP = \alpha$. Then we define the dilatation σ to have vertex V, and to be such that

$$\sigma(P) = P'.$$

Suppose that $\sigma(Q) = P^*$. Then

$$P^* = \sigma(Q) = \sigma\tau(P) = \sigma\tau\sigma^{-1}(P').$$

But, by construction, since PQ represents τ, the segment $P'P^*$ represents the translation τ^α. Hence

$$\tau^\alpha = \sigma\tau\sigma^{-1}.$$

As a hint of the possibilities which are to be found in translations, let τ_1 and τ_2 be two distinct translations, in different directions. Take any point O in the plane, and let $\tau_1(O) = E$, and $\tau_2(O) = F$. Then

$$\tau_1^\alpha \tau_2^\beta(O) = P,$$

where the point P has the coordinates (α, β) referred to the axes OE and OF, the point E being taken as $(1, 0)$, and the point F as $(0, 1)$.

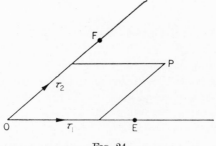

Fig. 24

Coordinates will be introduced in Ch. VI. The treatment will be completely abstract. The above indication of a method for introducing coordinates by using homomorphisms should prepare the reader for Artin's development [1]. We shall use the method of Marshall Hall [9].

CHAPTER II

THE DESARGUES AND PAPPUS THEOREMS

1. Incidence properties

In this chapter we shall be considering some geometrical constructs which occur in two or three dimensions, and we therefore begin with an account of what we expect from points and lines in a plane, and points, lines and planes in space of three dimensions. In other words, we discuss the *incidence properties* of two and three-dimensional space.

In the plane, all we ask is the following:

There shall exist points and lines, with a possible binary relation between them: a line may *contain* (*pass through*) a point, which shall be equivalent to the point *lying on* the line.

Two distinct points shall determine a unique line, which contains both points;

Two distinct lines shall determine a unique point, which lies on both lines.

This is the projective point of view, in which two lines always meet. We also assume, until the next chapter, the existence of as many points and lines as are necessary for our constructions.

In three dimensions we assume the existence of points, lines and planes, a plane being determined by three non-collinear points, which it contains. We also assume that the line joining two points of a plane lies in that plane, and that a line meets a plane in just one point, or is contained in it. From these two properties we may prove that two planes intersect in a line, or coincide, and that three planes meet in a point, or a line, or coincide.

A more formal statement of the incidence properties of space of n dimensions will be given later (Ch. X).

2. Configurations

In plane geometry we often come across geometrical constructs of points and lines which are such that every line of the construct contains a fixed number m, say, of points, and through every point of the figure there pass a fixed number n, say, of lines. We call such a construct an (m, n) *configuration*.

A triangle is evidently a $(2, 2)$ configuration. If we take four points, no three of which are collinear, we obtain six joins of pairs of points, and have a $(2, 3)$ configuration. We note that we may choose which points and lines of the figure are to be regarded as part of the configuration.

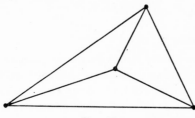

FIG. 25

We shall now examine two $(3, 3)$ configurations, the Desargues and the Pappus configurations. Both play a fundamental part in the development of projective geometry. The Desargues figure contains 10 points and 10 lines, whereas the Pappus figure contains 9 points and 9 lines. We have already come across the Desargues theorem on perspective triangles (Ch. I, p. 6):

1. *If two triangles are such that the joins of corresponding vertices are concurrent, then the intersection of corresponding sides are collinear.*

We have not yet proved this theorem. But we shall show in a moment that this theorem can be proved if the two triangles are

(a) not in the same plane, or

(b) in the same plane, which lies in three-dimensional space.

We shall then show that the theorem is not necessarily true in a plane, by constructing a plane geometry for which the propositions of incidence are true, but Desargues' theorem is not true.

But for the moment we merely wish to examine the configuration which results when the plane theorem is assumed to be true.

3. The Desargues configuration

The two triangles ABC and $A'B'C'$ are such that the joins of corresponding vertices AA', BB' and CC' pass through the point V, and corresponding sides $BC, B'C'$ meet at L, $CA, C'A'$ at M, and $AB, A'B'$ meet at N. There are 10 points in the figure, and 10 lines, and these form a $(3, 3)$ configuration (see Fig. 26).

Although we began with two definite triangles, and a vertex of perspective, the Desargues configuration is perfectly symmetrical in the sense that, once we have obtained it, we may take any point in the configuration as a vertex of perspective, and we can then find two triangles in the configuration which are in perspective from this point. The corresponding sides of these two triangles will intersect

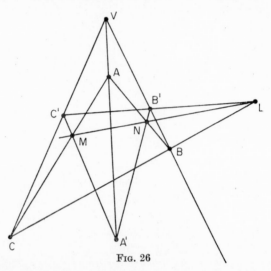

Fig. 26

in the three remaining points of the configuration. This becomes clearer if we adopt the notation for points and lines shown in the figure opposite, Fig. 27.

We take the five symbols 1, 2, 3, 4 and 5, and pair them thus, (12), (23), etc. This produces ten pairs, since we assume that $(ij) = (ji)$. We use these new symbols for points of the configuration, the points on a line being the three pairs which can be formed from three symbols, such as (12), (23) and (31).

The points on a line use up three integers of the five we are using. The line itself can be represented by the remaining two. Thus the line which carries the points (12), (23) and (31) can be represented by the symbol [45]. The symbols [45], [53] and [34] represent three lines through a point, the point (12), and so on.

Suppose now that we start with the point (45) as vertex of perspective, and try to find two appropriate triangles. The pairs of points collinear with this point are

(52) and (24),   (15) and (41),   and   (34) and (53).

We must choose two triangles whose sides are already part of the configuration, and this means that the symbols for the three vertices of a triangle must have an integer in common. Thus, if we start with the point (52), the other vertices must be (15) and (53), and the second triangle is (24), (41) and (34). The three corresponding sides of these two triangles meet at the collinear points (31), (23) and (21) respectively.

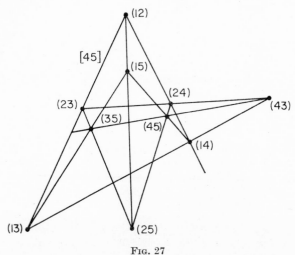

FIG. 27

The reader will naturally wonder where this symbolism comes from. It arises from considering the Desargues configuration as a plane section of the construct formed by five points in space of three dimensions. If we number these points 1, 2, 3, 4 and 5, the ten joins in pairs can be denoted by (12), (23), and so on. The plane determined by the points 1, 2 and 3 can be denoted by the symbol [45], and so on. It is a simple but worth-while exercise to show that a plane section of this three-dimensional construct gives the 10 points and lines of the Desargues configuration. The only properties required are the incidence properties of three-dimensional space described at the beginning of this chapter.

We now prove that:

2. *The Desargues theorem implies the dual theorem.*

The dual theorem says that if two triangles are such that their corresponding sides intersect in collinear points, then the joins of corresponding vertices are concurrent.

Using the symbolism of Fig. 27, we assume that the lines joining corresponding vertices (15) and (25), and (14) and (24) meet in (12), and wish to prove that the points (13), (23) are collinear with (12).

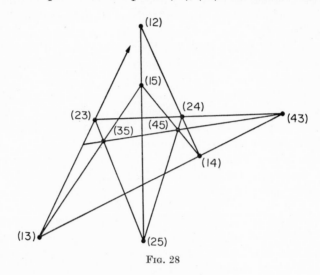

FIG. 28

Now, the triangles (24), (14), (34) and (25), (15), (35) are in perspective from the point (45), by virtue of the given conditions. Corresponding sides intersect in the points (12), (13) and (23). By the Desargues theorem, these points are collinear, which is what we wish to prove.

Similarly, the assumption of the dual theorem implies the truth of the Desargues theorem.

4. Desargues in three dimensions

Before constructing a non-Desarguesian geometry, we consider the two cases where we can *prove* the truth of the theorem.

If the two triangles ABC, $A'B'C'$ are not in the same plane, and AA', BB' and CC' all pass through V, then the points V, B, B', C, C' are coplanar. Hence the lines BB', CC' intersect. This point of intersection lies in the plane ABC, and also in the plane $A'B'C'$. It must therefore lie on the line of intersection of these two planes. Similarly the lines $CA, C'A'$ intersect, and $AB, A'B'$ intersect, and the three intersections being on the intersection of two planes, they are collinear.

We now assume that the two triangles $ABC, A'B'C'$ are coplanar, but that this common plane lies in a three-dimensional space. Denote the common plane by π. Through V draw a line which does not lie in π, and on it take two points, S and S', distinct from each other and from V.

The lines $SA, S'A'$ are coplanar, lying in the plane VSA, and therefore intersect in a point, which we call A^*. Similarly the lines $SB, S'B'$ meet in B^*, and $SC, S'C'$ meet in C^*. The points A^*, B^* and C^* do not lie in the plane π, since S is not in π. Nor are they collinear, since, if they were, the plane joining them to S would contain A, B and C, and therefore A, B, C would be collinear, contrary to hypothesis. Hence we have a triangle $A^*B^*C^*$ in perspective from S with the triangle ABC, and the two triangles are not coplanar. The sides of $A^*B^*C^*$ therefore meet the corresponding sides of ABC in the points of a line, the line of intersection of the plane $A^*B^*C^*$ with the plane π.

Now the same argument applies to the triangle $A'B'C'$ and the triangle $A^*B^*C^*$. The line B^*C^* meets the plane π in just one point, and this is the point where B^*C^* meets BC, and also the point where B^*C^* meets $B'C'$. Hence the intersections of corresponding sides of ABC and $A'B'C'$ are collinear, the line of collinearity being the intersection of the planes $A^*B^*C^*$ and the plane π.

Exercises

1. In the Desargues configuration show, by choosing A' as the centre of perspective, that the specializations "A' on BC" and "V on MN" are equivalent.

By choosing the point B as centre of perspective, show that the specializations "A' on BC" and "L on AA'" are equivalent.

2. Three triangles $A_i B_i C_i$ ($i = 1, 2, 3$) are such that any two of them are in perspective, the centre of perspective of $A_i B_i C_i$ and $A_j B_j C_j$ being V_{ij}. If V_{12}, V_{23} and V_{31} are collinear, prove that the three triangles have a common axis of perspective l, and that any two of the triangles $A_1 A_2 A_3$, $B_1 B_2 B_3$ and $C_1 C_2 C_3$ are in perspective, the three centres of perspective lying on l.

3. If the sides of a variable triangle pass through three fixed collinear points, while two vertices move along fixed lines, prove that the third vertex must move along a third fixed line concurrent with the other two.

5. A non-Desarguesian geometry

We now show that it is possible to set up a geometry in a plane with Points and Lines which satisfy the axioms of incidence for a plane, but not the theorem of Desargues. This construction is due to F. R. Moulton.

We consider a Euclidean plane referred to the rectangular
Cartesian coordinates (x, y), and in it a certain set of loci, which we
call L-loci. An L-locus is defined by the equation

$$y = mf(y, m)(x - a),$$

where m, a are real numbers, and $f(y, m)$ is defined as follows:

    (i)   if $m \leqslant 0$, $f(y, m) = 1$;

   (ii) if $m > 0$, $f(y, m) = 1$,   when $y < 0$,

                            $f(y, m) = \frac{1}{2}$,   when $y \geqslant 0$.

We also include the case $m = \infty$, the line $x = a$ being an L-locus,
and $m = 0$, $a = \infty$, the line $y = b$ being an L-locus.

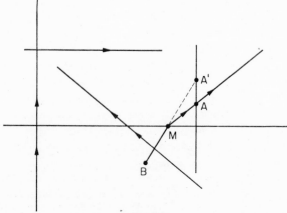

Fig. 29

These L-loci are not as complicated as they appear to be from
their equation. Quite simply, the idea is to refract all lines with
positive slope at the x-axis, and to allow all lines with infinite or
negative slope to pass unrefracted. It is clear that an L-locus is
completely determined by that part of it which lies in the region
$y \geqslant 0$, or by that part which lies in $y \leqslant 0$. Moreover, if an L-locus
has $m > 0$ (and is therefore not a line), the line joining any two points
of it has positive slope. Bearing these two facts in mind, it is easy
to see that there is an L-locus joining any two points A, B of the
plane, and that it is uniquely determined by these points.

In fact, if A and B both lie in $y \geqslant 0$, the upper half of the L-locus
is the upper half-line through A and B; and this determines the

L-locus uniquely. A similar result holds if A and B both lie in $y \leqslant 0$. Suppose now that A lies in the region $y > 0$, and B in $y < 0$. If the line AB has negative slope, the unique L-locus containing A and B is the line AB. If, finally, AB has positive slope, let A be the point (x_1, y_1), and let A' be the point $(x_1, 2y_1)$. Let $A'B$ meet $y = 0$ in M. Then the L-locus containing A and B is necessarily that determined by the half-line MA (see Fig. 29).

The first of our propositions of incidence for a plane has therefore been verified for points = Points, and Lines as defined above. We now show that any two distinct L-loci

$$y = mf(y, m)(x - a), \quad y = nf(y, n)(x - b)$$

$(m \neq n)$ have a unique point in common. This is evident if both m, n are negative, or, by the above remarks, if one of m, n is negative. If both m, n are positive and we solve the equations

$$y = m(x - a), \quad y = n(x - b),$$

we find that $\qquad y = mn(b - a)/(n - m);$

and solving the equations

$$y' = \tfrac{1}{2}m(x' - a), \quad y' = \tfrac{1}{2}n(x' - b),$$

we find that $\qquad y' = \tfrac{1}{2}mn(b - a)/(n - m).$

Thus y gives the intersection of the L-loci if $(b - a)/(n - m)$ is negative, and y' if this ratio is positive. We have therefore proved that any two distinct L-loci $(m \neq n)$ have a unique point in common.

If $m = n$ the L-loci do not meet, unless they coincide. They are then said to be *parallel*.

Our propositions of incidence were stated for a projective plane, but we have also described the process by which we pass from a Euclidean plane to a projective plane by the introduction of *ideal elements*, or *elements at infinity*. We can now follow a similar process to arrive at a set of elements for which the propositions of incidence are satisfied, but Desargues' theorem is not true. As we have already said, we distinguish the points and lines of this space from those of the original plane by calling them Points and Lines. The points of the Euclidean plane are Points. Corresponding to each set of parallel L-loci we postulate a further Point (at infinity) which is regarded as a Point of each locus of the set. The Lines are the L-loci of the Euclidean plane together with one other element, the Line at infinity, which contains all the Points at infinity. We now see that the Plane which contains these Points and Lines, and the Points and Lines themselves satisfy the propositions of incidence for a plane, viz. two points determine a line, two distinct lines determine a unique point.

In this Plane we now construct a figure which violates Desargues' theorem (Fig. 30).

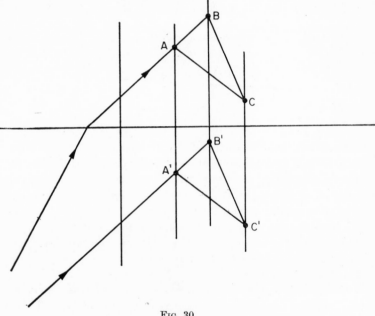

FIG. 30

The figure is self-explanatory. CB has negative slope and is parallel to $C'B'$; AC has negative slope and is parallel to $A'C'$. AA', BB' and CC' are respectively parallel to the y-axis. The two triangles are therefore in perspective. In Euclidean geometry corresponding sides would intersect on the line at infinity, and in our Plane CB meets $C'B'$ at infinity, and AC meets $A'C'$ at infinity. But the Line AB meets the Line $A'B'$ at a finite Point. Hence the Desargues theorem does not hold for the Plane we have constructed.

6. The Pappus configuration

We now introduce and study another fundamental configuration, the Pappus configuration, which is $(3,3)$ also, but only contains 9 points and 9 lines.

Let A, B, C and A', B', C' be two collinear sets of points. We consider the intersections L, M and N of the cross-joins (Fig. 31),

$$B'C \text{ and } BC', \quad C'A \text{ and } CA', \quad A'B \text{ and } AB'.$$

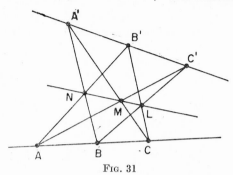

FIG. 31

It is assumed, of course, that the six initial points are coplanar. Now, in certain circumstances the points L, M and N are collinear. When this is the case we shall say: *Pappus' theorem is true.* To study the Pappus configuration we assume that the theorem is true, and add the line of collinearity to the configuration. This is then evidently $(3, 3)$, and contains 9 points and 9 lines.

We may also express Pappus' theorem in the following way:

3. *If alternate vertices of a hexagon lie on two lines, the three pairs of opposite sides meet in three collinear points.*

The dual of the Pappus theorem runs as follows:

4. *Let a, b, c and a', b', c' be two concurrent sets of lines. Then the joins l, m and n of the cross-intersections*

$$b'c \text{ and } bc', \quad c'a \text{ and } ca', \quad a'b \text{ and } ab'$$

are concurrent.

Figure 32 on p. 34 shows that this configuration is contained in the Pappus configuration, and that:

5. *The dual theorem follows from the Pappus theorem.*

We take A and A' as the points through which the lines a, b, c and a', b', c' respectively pass, and write $B' = ac'$, $C' = bc'$, $B = b'c$, $C = a'c$. Then the line l is the join BC', the line m is the join $B'C$, and the line n is the join MN. To show that l, m and n are concurrent, we have to show that L, M and N are collinear, and this is the content of Pappus' theorem.

The Pappus configuration may be regarded (in six ways) as consisting of a cycle of three triangles such that the three sides of each pass through the three vertices of the next. One such cycle consists of the triangles

$$ABN, \quad CA'B', \quad MC'L.$$

The others are easily picked out.

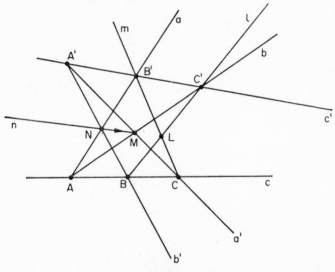

The Pappus configuration also contains pairs of triangles which are in triple perspective. For example, consider the triangles BMB' and NCC'. The sides of these triangles are not part of the configuration. The joins of corresponding vertices, namely the lines BN, MC and $B'C'$, are in the configuration and pass through A'. The same triangles, but with a rearrangement of vertices, namely BMB' and $CC'N$, are in perspective from the point A, and BMB' and $C'NC$ are in perspective from the point L.

7. A deduction from the Pappus theorem

Assuming the Pappus theorem we may prove the theorem implied above:

6. *If two triangles are doubly perspective, they are also triply perspective.*

There is no loss of generality in considering the triangles BMB' and NCC' in the figure above, and in assuming that both the given triangles and the pair of triangles BMB' and $CC'N$ are in perspective.

If the respective vertices of perspective are called A' and A, we then see that the assumption of the Pappus theorem leads to the triangles BMB' and $C'NC$ being in perspective from a point L, the points L, M and N being collinear by the Pappus theorem.

It is, of course, clear that the Pappus configuration has a high degree of symmetry. If we choose any two lines in the figure which do not intersect at a point of the configuration, the two triplets of points on these lines may be so chosen that the intersection of cross-joins gives us three collinear points of the configuration. For example, the triplets L, B', C and A', B, N produce the collinear set A, M, C'.

Exercises

1. Show that the Pappus theorem may be deduced from the Desargues theorem in the special case when the two triads of points are in perspective.

2. $ABCD$ is a parallelogram. A line parallel to AB intersects AD, BC in P, Q respectively, and a line parallel to AD intersects AB, CD in R, S respectively. Deduce, from the dual of the Pappus theorem, that PR meets QS on the diagonal BD.

8. Desargues from Pappus

We shall see at a later stage (Ch. VI, § 17) that the assumption of Pappus' theorem imposes important restrictions on the field of the coordinates which can be introduced into a plane, if we merely postulate the propositions of incidence and the Desargues theorem. But at the moment we are interested in proving:

7. *The Desargues theorem in a plane is a consequence of the Pappus theorem.*

We adopt another notation, just for the purposes of this proof, and suppose that the triangles $A_1 A_2 A_3$ and $B_1 B_2 B_3$ are in perspective from the point V, and that $A_2 A_3$ meets $B_2 B_3$ at P_1, that $A_3 A_1$ meets $B_3 B_1$ at P_2, and $A_1 A_2$ meets $B_1 B_2$ at P_3. We want to show that, assuming Pappus' theorem, the points P_1, P_2, P_3 are collinear.

The proof we give, based on the original Hessenberg proof, is correct in its broad outlines, but breaks down in certain special cases. We shall examine the possibilities of breakdown in a moment. First of all, let us consider the broad outlines of the proof (see Fig. 33).

9. The general proof in outline

We shall apply Pappus' theorem three times. Let Q be the intersection of $A_1 A_2$ and $B_2 B_3$ and consider the two triads of points

(A_3, B_3, V) and (Q, A_2, A_1). Then the three points X, E, P_1 are collinear, where X is the intersection of VA_2 and $A_1 B_3$, the point E is the intersection of VQ and $A_1 A_3$, and P_1 has already been defined. Now take the two triads (B_1, A_1, V) and (Q, B_2, B_3). Then Pappus' theorem shows that X, F, P_3 are collinear, where the new point F is the intersection of VQ and $B_1 B_3$. Finally, consider the two triads (F, Q, E) and (A_1, X, B_3). Pappus' theorem now shows that the points P_1, P_2 and P_3 are collinear, since FX meets $A_1 Q$ at P_3, FB_3 meets EA_1 at P_2, and EX meets QB_3 at P_1.

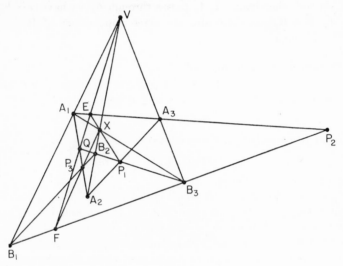

FIG. 33

10. Breakdown of proof

If we look at Pappus' theorem again, as enunciated on p. 33, we see that it has meaning if the points A, B, C are distinct, and likewise the points A', B', C', none of these six points lying at the intersection of the two lines on which the triads lie. If these conditions are not satisfied, we do not obtain any information about the collinearity of three distinct points, and although the statement that L, M, N are collinear, where, say, $M = N$, is not false, it is not helpful either. If, say, both A and B' are at the intersection of the two lines containing the triads, the line AB' is indeterminate, but the Pappus theorem merely says that three points on the line $A'B$ are collinear, and this is not useful information.

In the above proof, therefore, we must exercise care in seeing that Pappus' theorem can be applied in a meaningful manner. Now, it is possible that $B_2 B_3$ may pass through A_1. In such a case $Q = A_1$, and in our first application of Pappus' theorem the triad (Q, A_2, A_1) does not consist of distinct points. This breakdown might not invalidate the proof if the other two applications of the Pappus theorem were meaningful. But we see that the other two applications also break down, since in the second application QA_1 is not defined, and in the third we have $Q = E$.

If, on the other hand, $A_1 A_2$ passes through B_3, we have $Q = B_3$, $E = A_3$, $F = B_3$, and here also the three applications of Pappus produce nothing.

11. Preparation for general proof

We now give a proof, by Arno Cronheim [7], which considers these possibilities. For conciseness we shall write

$$(X, Y, Z)$$

whenever the points X, Y, Z are collinear, and

$$\text{non}\,(X, Y, Z)$$

when they are not collinear.

We assume that the seven points A_1, A_2, A_3, B_1, B_2, B_3 and V are all distinct, that the three lines $VA_1 B_1$, $VA_2 B_2$ and $VA_3 B_3$ are distinct, and that neither (A_1, A_2, A_3) nor (B_1, B_2, B_3), in other words, each triad is a proper triad. These are the assumptions we made before, of course. We now prove two lemmas which are independent of the Pappus property.

LEMMA 1. $\text{non}\,(A_i, B_i, B_k)$ and $\text{non}\,(A_i, A_k, B_k)$ for $i \neq k$.

Since $VA_i B_i \neq VA_k B_k$, for $i \neq k$, this is immediate.

LEMMA 2. If there does not exist a permutation (i, j, k) of the numbers $(1, 2, 3)$ such that $\text{non}\,(A_i, B_j, B_k)$ and $\text{non}\,(B_k, A_i, A_j)$ simultaneously, then either (A_x, B_y, B_z) for all permutations (x, y, z), or (B_x, A_y, A_z) for all permutations (x, y, z).

Without loss of generality we may assume that $\text{non}\,(B_1, A_2, A_3)$. By hypothesis we cannot have $\text{non}\,(A_2, B_1, B_3)$, nor can we have $\text{non}\,(A_3, B_1, B_2)$; so (A_2, B_1, B_3) and (A_3, B_1, B_2). But if we had (B_3, A_1, A_2), this, together with (A_2, B_1, B_3), would give (A_1, A_2, B_1), which contradicts the first lemma. Therefore we have $\text{non}\,(B_3, A_1, A_2)$, and by hypothesis we cannot have $\text{non}\,(A_1, B_2, B_3)$, so we have (A_1, B_2, B_3).

From non (B_1, A_2, A_3) we have therefore deduced:

$$(A_2, B_1, B_3), \quad (A_3, B_1, B_2), \quad (A_1, B_2, B_3).$$

This proves the lemma, since if we began with non (A_1, B_2, B_3) we should have found:

$$(B_1, A_2, A_3), \quad (B_2, A_1, A_3), \quad (B_3, A_1, A_2).$$

12. General proof in detail

We can now proceed with the proof of Desargues in two stages. In the first we avoid the special case in which the classical proof breaks down.

Case 1. There exists a permutation (i, j, k) such that non (A_i, B_j, B_k) and non (B_k, A_i, A_j).

We assume that non (A_1, B_2, B_3) and non (B_3, A_2, A_1). We retrace the steps of the proof given above, but this time we must justify our tacit assumptions.

We define Q to be the intersection of $A_1 A_2$ and $B_2 B_3$. Since non (A_1, B_2, B_3), $Q \neq A_1$. Since non (A_2, B_2, B_3), $Q \neq A_2$. Since non (A_3, B_2, B_3), $Q \neq A_3$.

Since non (B_1, B_2, B_3), $Q \neq B_1$. Since non (A_1, B_2, A_2), $Q \neq B_2$. Since non (B_3, A_2, A_1), $Q \neq B_3$. If $Q = V$, we should have (V, A_1, A_2), but $VA_1 \neq VA_2$, by hypothesis. Hence our first constructed point Q is distinct from the seven points A_i, B_i and V.

Now consider the two triads (A_3, B_3, V) and (Q, A_2, A_1). By what we have just proved, we have six distinct points here, and since non (A_1, A_2, A_3), they lie on distinct lines. If any one of the six points was at the intersection of these two lines, we should have either:

$$(A_3, A_2, A_1), \quad \text{or} \quad (B_3, A_2, A_1), \quad \text{or} \quad (V, A_2, A_1),$$

which possibilities must all be rejected, or

$$(Q, A_3, B_3), \quad \text{or} \quad (A_2, A_3, B_3), \quad \text{or} \quad (A_1, A_3, B_3).$$

Since Q lies on $B_2 B_3$, and $B_2 B_3 \neq A_3 B_3$, since $VB_2 \neq VB_3$, the possibility (Q, A_3, B_3) together with (Q, B_2, B_3) would lead to $Q = B_3$, which is not the case. The other two possibilities are excluded by the first lemma.

The Pappus theorem can therefore be applied to the two triads (A_3, B_3, V) and (Q, A_2, A_1), and we obtain three collinear points, (X, E, P_1), where X is the intersection of VA_2 and $A_1 B_3$ and E is the intersection of VQ and $A_1 A_3$.

Now consider the triples (B_1, A_1, V) and (Q, B_2, B_3). These six points are distinct, and lie on distinct lines, since non (B_1, B_2, B_3). Once again, we must check to see whether any one of the six points can lie at the intersection of the two lines. We can dismiss the possibilities:

$$(B_1, B_2, B_3), \quad (A_1, B_2, B_3), \quad (V, B_2, B_3),$$

and we have

$$(Q, B_1, A_1), \quad (B_2, B_1, A_1), \quad (B_3, B_1, A_1)$$

left. Since Q is on $A_1 A_2 \neq A_1 B_1$, and $Q \neq A_1$, we cannot have (Q, B_1, A_1), and the last two possibilities cannot be realized, by the first lemma.

Applying the Pappus theorem to (B_1, A_1, V) and (Q, B_2, B_3) we find that the points X, F, P_3 are collinear, where F is the intersection of VQ and $B_1 B_3$.

Finally, we consider the triads (F, Q, E) and (A_1, X, B_3). We first show that none of the points F, Q and E lies on $A_1 B_3$. If (Q, A_1, B_3), then since also (Q, B_2, B_3), we should deduce that (A_1, B_2, B_3), which is not the case. To exclude (E, A_1, B_3), we first prove that $E \neq A_1$. If $E = A_1$, then necessarily $Q = A_1$, since (V, Q, E), and Q lies on $A_1 A_2$. But we know that $Q \neq A_1$, so that $E \neq A_1$. Since $E \neq A_1$, if (E, A_1, B_3) is combined with (E, A_1, A_3), it would follow that (A_1, A_3, B_3), which is not the case. To show that non (F, A_1, B_3) we consider (F, A_1, B_3) together with (F, B_1, B_3). If we can show that $F \neq B_3$, the assumption (F, A_1, B_3) would lead to (A_1, B_1, B_3), which is not the case. If $F = B_3$, then since (V, Q, F), and (Q, B_2, B_3), and $Q \neq B_3$, we would find that (V, B_2, B_3), which is not the case.

We now prove that A_1, X and B_3 are distinct. If $X = A_1$, we should have $VA_1 = VB_2$, which is not the case. If $X = B_3$, then $VB_2 = VB_3$, which is not the case.

So far we have proved that the lines containing the triads under consideration, (F, Q, E) and (A_1, X, B_3), are distinct, that none of the points F, Q or E lies at the intersection of the two lines, and that A_1, X, B_3 are distinct. To show that we obtain a well-defined Pappus configuration, we must be as thorough as we have already been in the first two cases, and show, if we can, that F, Q and E are distinct, and that none of the points A_1, X and B_3 lies on the line FQE.

Cronheim does not do this, and we shall show, in fact, that it is possible for this final Pappus configuration to become specialized, adding nothing to our information. Fortunately we shall still be able to deduce the Desargues theorem from the first two applications of Pappus.

We consider the possibilities:

$E = Q$: Since (V, E, Q), and E lies on $A_1 A_3$ while Q lies on $A_1 A_2$, this can only be the case if $E = Q = A_1$, which has already been ruled out.

$Q = F$: Since (V, Q, F), and Q lies on $B_2 B_3$ while F lies on $B_1 B_3$, this can only be the case if $F = Q = B_3$, which has already been excluded.

$E = F$: Since (V, E, F), and E lies on $A_1 A_3$ while F lies on $B_1 B_3$, this can only be the case if $E = F = P_2$. There is no reason why this should not happen, as Fig. 34 shows.

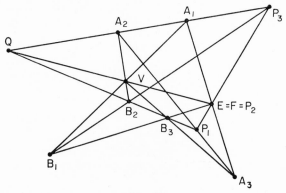

FIG. 34

In this case we have proved that (X, E, P_1) and (X, F, P_3) already, and if $E = F = P_2$ this gives (X, P_2, P_1) and (X, P_2, P_3). If $X \neq P_2$, it follows that (P_1, P_2, P_3), which is the Desargues theorem.

If $X = P_2$, then since (P_2, A_1, A_3) and (X, A_1, B_3) and $P_2 \neq A_1$ (since if $P_2 = A_1$ then (A_1, B_1, B_3)), we find that $X = P_2$ leads to (A_1, A_3, B_3) which is not the case.

The only other possibilities we must examine are:

(A_1, E, Q): This involves $E = Q = A_1$, excluded.

(X, E, Q): This involves $VEQ = VX = VB_2$. Since Q lies on $B_2 B_3$, this would give $Q = B_2$, which is not the case.

(B_3, E, Q): This would lead to $VB_3 = VQ$, and since Q lies on $B_2 B_3$, and $VB_2 \neq VB_3$, we should have $Q = B_3$, which is not the case.

Hence, except in the case considered above, there are no unforeseen coincidences, and we can apply Pappus' theorem to the triads (F, Q, E) and (A_1, X, B_3) and obtain the collinear points (P_1, P_2, P_3).

We have assumed that non (A_1, B_2, B_3) and non (B_3, A_2, A_1). We now have:

13. Proof in special case

Case 2. There does not exist a permutation (i, j, k) such that non (A_i, B_j, B_k) and non (B_k, A_i, A_j).

It follows from Lemma 2 that either (A_x, B_y, B_z) or (B_x, A_y, A_z) for all permutations (x, y, z). We may assume that

$$(A_1, B_2, B_3), \quad (A_2, B_1, B_3), \quad (A_3, B_1, B_2).$$

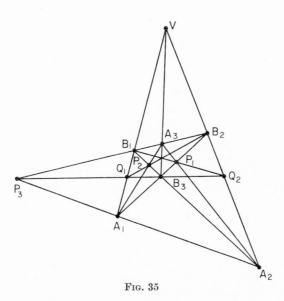

Fig. 35

As in Case 1, $P_i \neq A_k$ for all i, k, since neither (A_i, A_j, A_k) nor (A_j, B_j, B_k). Similarly, $P_i \neq B_k$. We define Q_1 to be the intersection of $B_3 P_3$ and $V A_1$, and Q_2 to be the intersection of $B_3 P_3$ and $V A_2$. Since P_3 is on $B_1 B_2$, but is distinct from B_1, B_2 and A_3, it follows that the line $B_3 P_3$ is distinct from the three lines $B_3 B_1 A_2$, $B_3 B_2 A_1$ and $B_3 A_3 V$. The points P_3, Q_1, Q_2 and V, and the six points A_i, B_i are therefore all distinct.

Consider the triads (V, A_3, B_3) and (P_3, A_2, A_1). Since

$$\text{non}\,(A_1, A_2, A_3),$$

they lie on distinct lines, and all six points are distinct. We leave to the reader the verification that no point of a triad lies on the line of the other triad. We therefore have a proper Pappus configuration, and the Pappus theorem shows that (P_2, Q_1, B_2). Similarly, considering the triads (V, A_3, B_3) and (P_3, A_1, A_2), we find that (P_1, Q_2, B_1). Finally, we consider (Q_1, A_1, B_1) and (A_2, Q_2, B_2). These triads satisfy the conditions for a meaningful application of Pappus' theorem, and since $A_1 B_1 \neq A_2 B_2$, P_1 is the intersection of $A_1 B_2$ and $Q_2 B_1$, P_2 is the intersection of $A_2 B_1$ and $Q_1 B_2$, and P_3 is the intersection of $Q_1 Q_2$ and $A_1 A_2$, so that (P_1, P_2, P_3) and, once again, the Desargues theorem is proved.

A shorter proof, using the consequences of Pappus' theorem, will be given later (Ch. III, § 20). We shall see, however, in Ch. III, § 21 that this shorter proof also breaks down and needs modification in special cases.

CHAPTER III

CONSEQUENCES OF THE PAPPUS THEOREM

1. Perspectivities

We now introduce a simple concept which is basic in any study of projective geometry, the notion of a *perspectivity* between the points on two lines. A few definitions first:

A set of points $P, Q, R, \ldots$ on a line l is called a *range* of points on l. A set of coplanar lines $p, q, r, \ldots$ through a point O is called a *pencil* of lines through O. From the propositions of incidence it follows that if O is any point not on l, and l' is any line in the plane joining O and l which does not pass through O, l' will intersect any line of the pencil $O(P, Q, R, \ldots)$ in a point, giving a range of points $P', Q', R', \ldots$ on l'. The ranges on l and l' are said to be *in perspective* from O, and we write

$$(P, Q, R, \ldots) \underset{\wedge}{\overset{O}{=}} (P', Q', R', \ldots).$$

Such a perspectivity establishes a one-to-one correspondence between the points on l and those on l'.

We propose to prove a number of theorems involving perspectivities. A number of modern texts seem to take pleasure in avoiding any mention of these fundamental one-to-one correspondences until a very late stage,

> . . . . scorning the base degrees
> By which [they] did ascend.

It is hardly possible to solve many problems in projective geometry without the use of perspective transformations, and we do not apologize for talking about them.

Some of the proofs which follow are long, because all possible cases have to be considered. So far we have tried not to be too pedantic in our attitude, and told the reader to assume that a sufficient number of points are at hand for the purpose of our proof. But we must consider the possibility of a plane, and therefore every line in it, containing only a finite number of points. We shall refuse to consider the case of any line containing less than three points, but even then things are not too easy. If, therefore, the reader should find some of the next sections tedious, he may pass over the details, having made certain that he sees what the theorems imply.

Returning to our consideration of perspective transformations, we see that if l contains only k points, l' contains only k points. Through O there pass exactly k lines, and through every point in the plane there pass exactly k lines. We add to our postulates of incidence the additional one:

Every line contains at least three points.†

Hence $k \geqslant 3$. We shall see that there are geometries in which a plane contains only a finite number of points, and our methods must be devised to take account of these *finite* geometries, especially when $k = 3$ (Ch. V, § 4).

2. Projective correspondence

Now let us suppose that another perspectivity has been established between the points of l' and those of a line l'', the vertex being O'.

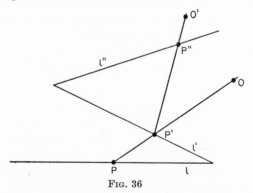

Fig. 36

The line l'' must cut l', but need not lie in the plane joining O to l, which we write $O(l)$. We describe the perspectivities thus:

$$(P, Q, R, \ldots) \underset{\overline{\wedge}}{\overset{O}{=}} (P', Q', R', \ldots) \underset{\overline{\wedge}}{\overset{O'}{=}} (P'', Q'', R'', \ldots).$$

† Later on (Ch. V, § 1) we shall replace this postulate by the following: *there is at least one set of four points, no three of which are collinear.*

If the geometry contains at least two lines, which we assume is the case, the two postulates are equivalent.

A one-to-one correspondence, which is not necessarily a perspectivity, has been set up between the ranges on l and l'', and we say that these ranges are *projectively related*, or simply that they are *related ranges*. We write

$$(P, Q, R, \ldots) \barwedge (P'', Q'', R'', \ldots)$$

in this case.

The process may be continued, and we say that *two ranges are related, or projective, if they can be put into a one-to-one correspondence by means of a finite chain of perspectivities.*

It is clear that in a perspectivity distinct points are projected into distinct points. Hence, if two ranges are related, distinct points in one range correspond to distinct points in the other range.

3. Freedom of a projective correspondence

An important problem in the theory of related ranges is to determine when two given ranges, which are in a one-to-one correspondence, are related by a series of perspectivities. The following theorem is a first step towards an answer. We shall use the term *projectivity* for *series of perspectivities*.

1. *Given two triplets of distinct points P_1, Q_1, R_1 and P_3, Q_3, R_3 lying, respectively, on two distinct lines l_1 and l_3, there is a projectivity which assigns P_1, Q_1, R_1 to P_3, Q_3, R_3 respectively.*

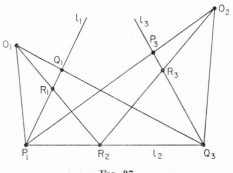

Fig. 37

Since P_1, Q_1, R_1 are distinct, and l_1 is distinct from l_3, at most one of these points lies on l_3. Similarly, at most one of the points P_3, Q_3, R_3 lies on l_1. Hence we can always choose one pair of points which are not required to correspond in the projectivity, say P_1 and Q_3, neither of which lies on both l_1 and l_3. Let $P_1 Q_3$ be the line l_2.

The join $Q_1 Q_3$ is distinct from l_1 and l_2. On it take a point O_1 which is not on either of these lines, and let $O_1 R_1$ meet l_2 in R_2 (O_1 and R_1 lie in the plane $O_1(l_2)$). Since l_3 and l_2 meet, $P_1 P_3$ and $R_2 R_3$ meet. Indeed, their intersection is unique, since $P_3 \neq R_3$, and $P_1 P_3$ has a single point in common with l_3. Let this intersection be O_2. (It is not necessarily distinct from O_1.) Then

$$(P_1, Q_1, R_1) \mathop{\overline{\wedge}}^{O_1} (P_1, Q_3, R_2) \mathop{\overline{\wedge}}^{O_2} (P_3, Q_3, R_3),$$

which proves the theorem.

An immediate corollary is that a projectivity which is the result of three perspectivities, at most, can be set up between two ranges on the *same* line, so that three distinct, arbitrarily chosen points correspond to three distinct, arbitrarily chosen points.

4. Main theorem on projective correspondences

It may be thought that the projectivity established between l_1 and l_3 is a special one, because it is the result of only *two* perspectivities. This is not the case, for we now prove:

2. *If a range of points on a line l_1 is related by a chain of m perspectivities to a range of points on a line $l_{m+1} \neq l_1$, this projectivity is equivalent to at most two perspectivities.*

We prove this result, the main theorem of this section, in stages. From this point we must assume Desargues' theorem to be true, so that our theorem will be based on:

(a) the propositions of incidence,

(b) every line contains at least three points,

(c) Desargues' theorem.

We consider a sequence of two perspectivities between the lines l_1 and l_2 and l_2 and l_3. We shall call l_2 the *intermediary line* for the projectivity between l_1 and l_3. Now l_1 and l_2 must intersect: let them meet in the point L_{12}, and let l_2, l_3 intersect in the point L_{23}; the points L_{12} and L_{23} may or may not coincide. If they do, we prove the theorem in the next section.

5. A product of perspectivities

3. *If l_1, l_2 and l_3 are concurrent, and $l_1 \neq l_3$, the sequence of the two perspectivities between the points of l_1 and l_3 is equivalent to a single perspectivity.*

Let

$$(P_1, Q_1, R_1, \ldots) \underset{\overline{\wedge}}{\overset{O_{12}}{=}} (P_2, Q_2, R_2, \ldots),$$

and

$$(P_2, Q_2, R_2, \ldots) \underset{\overline{\wedge}}{\overset{O_{23}}{=}} (P_3, Q_3, R_3, \ldots).$$

There is nothing to prove if $O_{12} = O_{23}$, so we may suppose that $O_{12} \neq O_{23}$. We consider the triads $P_1 P_2 P_3$ and $Q_1 Q_2 Q_3$, and we see that these are in perspective from $L_{12} = L_{23}$. If both triads are proper triangles, we may use Desargues' theorem, and the sides

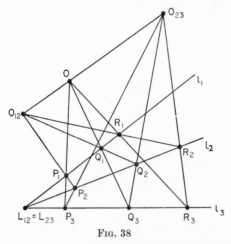

FIG. 38

$P_1 P_3$ and $Q_1 Q_3$ intersect on the join $O_{12} O_{23}$ of the two centres of perspective at a point O, say. Hence $Q_1 Q_3$, and similarly $R_1 R_3$, passes through O, the intersection of $O_{12} O_{23}$ with $P_1 P_3$. Thus

$$(P_1, Q_1, R_1, \ldots) \underset{\overline{\wedge}}{\overset{O}{=}} (P_3, Q_3, R_3, \ldots).$$

If the points P_1, P_2, P_3 are collinear, which is the case when P_1 lies on $O_{12} O_{23}$, the point O may be taken at the intersection of $Q_1 Q_3$ with $O_{12} O_{23} = P_1 P_2 P_3$. If both sets of points P_1, P_2, P_3 and Q_1, Q_2, Q_3 are collinear, then we must have $O_{12} = O_{23}$.

6. Replacement of intermediary line

If, on the other hand, $L_{12} \neq L_{23}$, we have

4. *In the sequence of two perspectivities between the points of l_1 and l_3, the intermediary line may be replaced by any other line l_2^**

which joins a pair of points on l_1 and l_3 which are neither corresponding nor coincident.

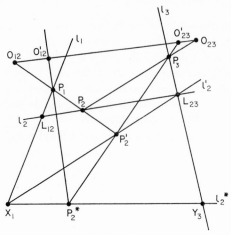

FIG. 39

We apply the previous theorem twice. Let l_2^* be the line joining X_1 of l_1 to Y_3 of l_3. By hypothesis, X_1 and Y_3 are distinct, and do not correspond in the projectivity between l_1 and l_3. Let us suppose, in the first place, that X_1 does not correspond to L_{23}, the intersection of l_2 and l_3. Since L_{23} is self-corresponding in the perspectivity, centre O_{23}, between l_2 and l_3, we deduce that $X_1 L_{23}$ does not pass through O_{12}. We take the line $X_1 L_{23}$ as l_2'. It satisfies the requirements of our theorem, since X_1 and L_{23} are not corresponding points.

We can project the range $(P_2, \dots)$ on l_2 from O_{12} into the range $(P_2', \dots)$ on l_2'. For l_2' lies in the plane $L_{23}(l_1) = O_{12}(l_1)$. By a sequence of two perspectivities, vertices O_{12} and O_{23}, we have set up a projectivity between the ranges $(P_2', \dots)$ on l_2' and $(P_3, \dots)$ on l_3, and the lines l_2', l_2, l_3 are concurrent. By the previous theorem there is a point O_{23}' on $O_{12} O_{23}$ such that

$$(P_1, \dots) \underset{\wedge}{\overset{O_{12}}{=\!=}} (P_2', \dots) \underset{\wedge}{\overset{O_{23}'}{=\!=}} (P_3, \dots).$$

Similarly, since X_1 and Y_3 are not corresponding points, and X_1 is self-corresponding in the perspectivity, centre O_{12}, between l_1 and l_2', the line $X_1 Y_3 = l_2^*$ does not pass through O_{23}'. If we now project the range $(P_2', \dots)$ on l_2' into the range $(P_2^*, \dots)$ on l_2^* from the point O_{23}' then again, by the previous theorem, since l_2^*, l_2' and l_1 are concurrent, there exists a point O'_{12} on $O_{12}O'_{23}$ and therefore on $O_{12}O_{23}$ such that

$$(P_1, \ldots) \underset{\wedge}{\overset{O'_{12}}{\doubleequals}} (P_2^*, \ldots) \underset{\wedge}{\overset{O'_{23}}{\doubleequals}} (P_3, \ldots).$$

The line l_2^* therefore satisfies the requirements of our theorem, and may be used instead of l_2 as an intermediary line.

If X_1 corresponds to L_{23}, the argument fails. If L_{12} does *not* correspond to Y_3, we can prove the theorem, as above, by taking $L_{12}Y_3$ in place of l'_2 as the first intermediary line used in our argument. There remains the case in which X_1 corresponds to L_{23}, and L_{12} corresponds to Y_3. We consider this case.

On l_1 there exists at least one other point besides L_{12} and X_1. Let T_1 be such a point. If l_3 meets l_1, and T_1 is the point of intersection, the point T_3 of l_3 which corresponds to T_1 is different from T_1, unless the join $O_{12}O_{23}$ of the centres of perspective passes through T_1. Suppose that $O_{12}O_{23}$ passes through T_1, and that $T_1 = T_3$. There are two possibilities:

(i) There is a point Z_3 on l_3 distinct from T_3, L_{23}, Y_3. We can pass from the intermediary line l_2 to the intermediary line l_2^* by taking as intermediary lines, in order,

$$L_{12}L_{23}, \quad L_{12}Z_3, \quad Z_3X_1, \quad X_1Y_3,$$

none of which joins corresponding points, or passes through the intersection of l_1 and l_3.

(ii) Every line contains only three points. Then the ranges on l_1 and l_3 are in perspective from the intersection of X_1L_{23} and Y_3L_{12}, and this point is $O_{12} = O_{23}$. The case in which $O_{12} = O_{23}$ is, of course, trivial.

Finally, if l_1 and l_3 meet, and T_3 and T_1 are different, or if l_1 and l_3 do not meet, and T_3 corresponds to T_1, we replace Z_3 by T_3 in the proof of (i), above. This concludes the proof of Theorem 4.

7. Completion of proof of main theorem

We are now in a position to complete the proof of our main theorem, Theorem 2, on the reduction in the number of perspectivities.

In order to do this we first consider the case of four lines l_1, l_2, l_3 and l_4, with ranges $(P_1, \ldots)$, $(P_2, \ldots)$, $(P_3, \ldots)$ and $(P_4, \ldots)$ on them, and suppose that

$$(P_1, \ldots) \underset{\wedge}{\overset{O_{12}}{\doubleequals}} (P_2, \ldots), \quad (P_2, \ldots) \underset{\wedge}{\overset{O_{23}}{\doubleequals}} (P_3, \ldots), \quad (P_3, \ldots) \underset{\wedge}{\overset{O_{34}}{\doubleequals}} (P_4, \ldots).$$

By the definition of perspective, l_1 and l_2 are distinct intersecting lines, and similarly so are l_2 and l_3, and l_3 and l_4; but other coincidences of the lines l_1, l_2, l_3 and l_4 which are consistent with these restrictions are possible, and must be taken into account.

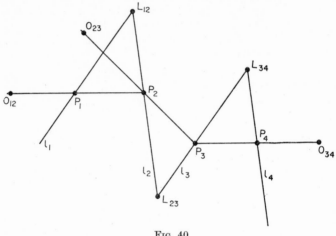

FIG. 40

We first prove that if l_1 and l_4 are distinct lines we can pass from the range $(P_1, \ldots)$ to the range $(P_4, \ldots)$ by two perspectivities. We first observe that in the case in which each line of the configuration contains only three points, the result follows by the argument used to prove Theorem 1. Indeed, the ranges on l_1 and l_4 each consist of three points and are in one-to-one correspondence. Using the argument adopted to prove Theorem 1 it follows at once that we can pass from the range on l_1 to the range on l_4 by two perspectivities.

In proving the result generally we may now confine ourselves to the case in which each line of the configuration contains at least four distinct points. We first consider the cases which arise when the lines l_1, l_2, l_3 and l_4 have certain special mutual relationships.

(i) l_1, l_2, l_3 distinct but concurrent. By Theorem 3 we can pass from $(P_1, \ldots)$ to $(P_3, \ldots)$ by one perspectivity, and the result follows at once.

(ii) l_2, l_3, l_4 distinct but concurrent. This case follows in exactly the same way as (i).

(iii) $l_1 = l_3, l_4$ not through $L_{12} = L_{23}$. Then there is a line l_3^* through L_{12}, different from l_3, which meets l_4 in a point different from a possible intersection of l_2 and l_4 and from the point of l_4 which corresponds to L_{12} on l_2. By Theorem 4 we may replace l_3 by l_3^*, and then apply (i).

(iv) $l_2 = l_4, l_1$ not through $L_{23} = L_{34}$. This case follows as in (iii).

(v) $l_1 = l_3$, $l_2 = l_4$. Let p be any line through $L_{12} = L_{23} = L_{34}$ different from $l_1 = l_3$, and from $l_2 = l_4$. From a point V_1 in the plane of l_1 and p we project the range $(P_1, ...)$ on l_1 into the range $(P, ...)$ on p. Then

$$(P, ...) \overset{V_1}{\overline{\wedge}} (P_1, ...) \overset{O_{12}}{\overline{\overline{\wedge}}} (P_2, ...) \overset{O_{23}}{\overline{\overline{\wedge}}} (P_3, ...) \overset{O_{34}}{\overline{\overline{\wedge}}} (P_4, ...).$$

Using Theorem 3 we obtain, in turn,

$$(P, ...) \overset{V_i}{\overline{\overline{\wedge}}} (P_i, ...) \quad (i = 1, 2, 3, 4)$$

for suitably chosen points V_2, V_3, V_4. Hence we have

$$(P_1, ...) \overset{V_1}{\overline{\overline{\wedge}}} (P, ...) \overset{V_4}{\overline{\overline{\wedge}}} (P_4, ...),$$

and indeed, by another application of Theorem 3, we see that the ranges on l_1 and l_4 are in perspective in this case.

We have now considered all the cases in which l_1, l_2, l_3 are concurrent, or l_2, l_3, l_4 are concurrent. The remaining cases are, first, the general case illustrated in Fig. 40, and the cases in which l_1, l_2, l_4 are concurrent (but all different) or l_1, l_3, l_4 are concurrent (but all different). These last possibilities cannot occur simultaneously; otherwise we should be in a case already considered. We need only consider the case in which l_1, l_2, l_4 are not concurrent (whether l_1, l_3, l_4 are concurrent or not), since the case in which l_1, l_2, l_4 are concurrent and l_1, l_3, l_4 are not concurrent is obtained by interchanging the rôles of l_2 and l_3. Our argument, of course, includes the general case.

Since l_1, l_2, l_4 are not concurrent, we may replace l_3 by a line l_3^* joining L_{12} to a point of l_4 not on l_2, nor corresponding, in the range on l_4, to L_{12} regarded as a point of l_2. We then have l_1, l_2, l_3^* concurrent, and may apply (i). This completes our proof of Theorem 2 in the case $m = 3$.

Now consider the general case of Theorem 2, for general m. The case in which each line has only three points can be dealt with as when $m = 3$, and may be omitted. If, in the sequence of lines

$$l_1, l_2, l_3, ..., l_{m+1} \quad (m > 2),$$

5

we can find a line l_i which is different from l_{i+3}, we can apply the case $m = 3$ to reduce the number of perspectivities. We proceed in this way until either we reach the case of two perspectivities or else

$$l_i = l_{i+3} \quad (i = 1, 2, ..., m-2).$$

In this case $m > 3$, since we have assumed $l_1 \neq l_{m+1}$. Then l_1, l_2, l_3 are distinct lines. We can, by Theorem 4, replace l_2 by a different line l_2^* without altering any other l_i. Then, since $l_2^* \neq l_5$, we can apply the result for $m = 3$ to shorten the sequence of perspectivities. Thus in all cases we can reduce the number of perspectivities to *two*, and our theorem is proved.†

Corollary: A one-to-one projective correspondence between two ranges on the same straight line can be obtained as the result of at most three perspectivities.

As the reader was warned, the above proof has turned out to be a long one. But the consequences, as we see later on (§17), are so far-reaching, and lead us so far on our way, that no apology is offered for what we have done. Even those developments of the subject which take pleasure in avoiding perspectivities find, somewhere or other, that at least one formidable proof has to be negotiated before the way is clear!

8. Harmonic conjugates

We saw above (Th. 1) that any three distinct points on a line are projectively related to any other three distinct points on another line. If the lines are the same line, we need three perspectivities instead of two to perform the mapping. There is an obvious advantage in discussing points which are bound up with three given points in an invariant manner, so that a perspective transformation does not affect the relation of the fourth point to the three given ones. Hence the importance of *harmonic conjugates*, which we now discuss. Here also we assume nothing beyond the postulates mentioned above (§1), and we must therefore consider all special cases.

On a line l take two distinct points A and B. If C is any point of l, we construct a new point D on l as follows (see Fig. 41):

In a plane π through l take three lines a, b, c, passing respectively through A, B, C, each distinct from l and not all meeting in one point. Since at least three distinct lines pass through every point in π, it is possible to choose a, b, c to satisfy these conditions.

† For a short proof, using coordinates, see Ch. VII, Th. 9, p. 162.

Let b and c meet in P, c and a in Q, and let a and b meet in the point R. Then A cannot coincide with P, nor B with Q. Since A, B, P, Q are coplanar points, and not collinear, AP and BQ meet in a point. Let this be S. Then S is distinct from R, since B is distinct from A. The line RS has a unique intersection, which we call D, with l. This point D is the one we seek.

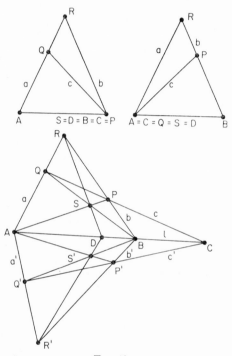

FIG. 41

It is immediately verified that if $C = B$, then $D = B$, and if $C = A$, then $D = A$. In these cases the construction of D does not depend on the particular set of lines a, b, c chosen.

We now prove that if C is distinct from A and B, the point D is independent of the coplanar set of lines a, b, c chosen: in other words

5. *D is determined only by the ordered triad A, B, C.*

We first examine the case in which there are only three points A, B, C on l. Then D must coincide with one of these points. If $D = A$, then R, S, Q, A must be collinear, and hence $Q = S$, or $Q = A$. If $Q = S$, then $R = P$, and a, b, c are concurrent, contrary to hypothesis: if $Q = A$, then $C = A$, which is again contrary to hypothesis. Similarly we cannot have $D = B$, and so the only remaining possibility is $D = C$. Hence, in this case too, the position of D does not depend on the particular choice of A, B, C.

We note that four points in a plane, no three of which are collinear, are said to form a quadrangle. The six joins of the vertices, taken in pairs, intersect in three other points besides the four given ones. These are called the *diagonal points* of the quadrangle. Thus, in Fig. 41 where A, B, P, Q are the vertices of the quadrangle, R, S and C are the diagonal points. When every line in a plane contains only three points, $C = D$, which means that *the diagonal points of every quadrangle are collinear*.

9. Independent of the construction

We may now confine ourselves to the case in which l (and hence every line) contains at least four points, and at least four coplanar lines pass through any point. We wish to show that the point D we have constructed is independent of the scaffolding used in the construction.

We consider any plane π', not necessarily distinct from π, through l, and in it we draw three lines a', b', c' through A, B, C respectively, these lines being distinct from l, and not concurrent. We repeat the construction given above, denoting the points corresponding to P, Q, R, S by P', Q', R', S'. Let $R'S'$ meet l in D'.

Consider, first of all, the case in which the lines a, a', b, b' and c, c' are all distinct. Corresponding sides of the triangles PQR, $P'Q'R'$ intersect in A, B, C, which are collinear. Hence, by the converse of Desargues' theorem (Ch. I, Th. 2), these triangles are in perspective. If $P = P'$, then $b = b'$, and $c = c'$, contrary to hypothesis; for similar reasons $Q \neq Q'$, and $R \neq R'$. Thus the lines PP', QQ' and RR' are determinate, and they must have a point V in common. If two of these lines coincide, say $QQ' = RR'$, then $QR = Q'R'$, that is, $a = a'$, which is contrary to hypothesis. Therefore V is determined by any two of the three lines.

Again, corresponding sides of the triangles PQS, $P'Q'S'$ intersect in B, A, C, and therefore these triangles are in perspective. Hence S, S' and V, the intersection of PP' and QQ', are collinear. The triangles QRS, $Q'R'S'$ are therefore in perspective from V. Let us assume, first of all, that $SQ \neq S'Q'$. Since SQ meets $S'Q'$ in B, and QR meets $Q'R'$ in A, Desargues' theorem shows that RS and $R'S'$ have a point in common on $BA = l$. Since RS meets l only in D, and $R'S'$ meets it only in D', it follows that $D = D'$.

If $SQ = S'Q'$, but $SP \neq S'P'$, we may use the triangles PRS, $P'R'S'$ in place of QRS, $Q'R'S'$, and prove that $D = D'$.

If $SQ = S'Q'$, and $SP = S'P'$, then $S = S'$, and QQ', PP' meet in S. Since PQR, $P'Q'R'$ are in perspective, RR' goes through $S = S'$. Hence $RS = R'S'$ meets l in the same point D.

This proof may break down if the lines a, a', b, b' and c, c' are not all distinct. For instance, if $c = c'$, the triangles PQR, $P'Q'R'$ are in perspective from the intersection of RR' with c, and PQS, $P'Q'S'$ are in perspective from the intersection of SS' with c, but since $PP' = QQ'$, we cannot deduce from these facts that QRS, $Q'R'S'$ are in perspective. We must therefore modify our proof.

We note that if $c = c'$, the planes π, π' coincide. We show that if the lines a, a', b, b', c, c' are not all distinct then there exists at least one set of lines a^*, b^*, c^* through A, B, C satisfying the requirements of the construction, such that a, a^*, b, b^*, c, c^*, and a', a^*, b', b^*, c', c^* are distinct sets of lines. The case in which $c = c'$ is typical.

Since through each point of l there pass at least four distinct lines of π, we can find lines a^* and b^* through A and B respectively distinct from l, a, a' and l, b, b' respectively. Let b^* meet a^* in R^*. Since $c = c'$, there is at least one line c^* in π which passes through C and is distinct from $c = c'$, l and CR^*. The lines a^*, b^*, c^* satisfy our requirements. We use them to construct a point D^*. By the proof given above, $D = D^*$, and similarly $D' = D^*$. It follows at once that $D = D'$.

10. Symmetry of harmonic relationship

This unique point D is called *the harmonic conjugate of C with respect to A and B*, and is denoted by

$$D = (A, B)/C.$$

It is clear from the construction that

$$D = (B, A)/C.$$

We now prove that this relation is not only symmetrical between A and B, but also between C and D, that is:

6. $$C = (A, B)/D = (B, A)/D.$$

To construct the harmonic conjugate of D with respect to A and B we draw three lines AQR, BSQ, DSR through A, B, D respectively to form a triangle QSR. Then BR and AS intersect in P, and QP meets l in the harmonic conjugate of D with respect to A and B (or B and A). This is the point C, so that the result is proved.

Exercise

1. If $D = (A, B)/C$, and A, B are kept fixed, prove that $(C)\barwedge(D)$. If A, C are kept fixed, prove that $(B)\barwedge(D)$.

11. Invariance of harmonic relationship

We have now established the uniqueness of the point $(A, B)/C$, and move on to the theorem:

7. *The relation of harmonic conjugacy is a projective invariant.*

We have seen that a projectivity can be established between the points A, B, C and the points A', B', C', these being two triads of collinear points (Th. 1). We now prove that such a projectivity makes $(A, B)/C$ correspond to $(A', B')/C'$.

If, in fact, $C = A$ or $C = B$, then we must have $C' = A'$ or $C' = B'$, and in these cases the result is evident. We therefore suppose that A, B, C (and therefore A', B', C') are distinct. Since a projectivity is defined to be the result of a finite number of perspectivities, we need only consider ranges A, B, C, A', B', C' on distinct lines l, l' which are in perspective.

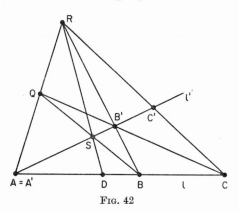

FIG. 42

We consider three special cases first:

(i) $A = A'$. Let the ranges be in perspective from R. To construct $D = (A, B)/C$ we draw the lines AR, BB', CB' through A, B, C

respectively to form the triangle $B'QR$. Since AB', BQ meet in S, the line RS meets l in the required point D.

To construct $D' = (A', B')/C'$, we draw through A', B', C' the lines $A'QR$, $B'QC$ and $C'CR$ respectively to form the triangle CRQ. Since $A'C$ and $B'R$ meet in B, the line BQ meets l' in D'. Therefore $D' = S$. Hence (A, B, C, D) and (A', B', C', D') are in perspective from R.

(ii) $B = B'$. This case follows at once from (i) since

$$(A, B)/C = (B, A)/C.$$

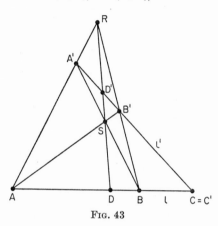

FIG. 43

(iii) $C = C'$. If AB' and $A'B$ meet in S, and RS meets l in D and l' in D', we construct $(A, B)/C$ by means of the lines AA', BB', $CA'B'$, and we construct $(A', B')/C'$ by means of the lines $A'A$, $B'B$ and CAB. It follows at once that $D = (A, B)/C$, and that $D' = (A', B')/C'$. Hence

$$(A, B, C, D) \underset{\wedge}{\overset{R}{=}} (A', B', C', D').$$

Finally, let l and l' meet in a point distinct from A, B, C and A', B', C', and suppose that (see Fig. 44)

$$(A, B, C, D) \underset{\wedge}{\overset{O}{=}} (A', B', C', D'),$$

where $D = (A, B)/C$. To prove that $D' = (A', B')/C'$, join CA', and let this line meet ODD' in D_1, and OBB' in B_1. Since

$$(A, B, C, D) \underset{\wedge}{\overset{O}{=}} (A', B_1, C, D_1),$$

and $D = (A, B)/C$, it follows from (iii) that $D_1 = (A', B_1)/C$, and since

$$(A', B_1, C, D_1) \underset{\overline{\wedge}}{\overset{O}{=}} (A', B', C', D'),$$

it follows from (i) that

$$D' = (A', B')/C'.$$

This concludes the proof of the theorem.

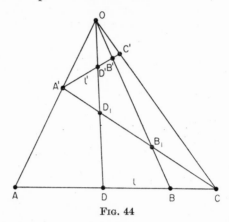

FIG. 44

Exercise

1. If A, B, C, D and A, B', C', D' are points of two distinct ranges, and $A = (C, D)/B = (C', D')/B'$, show that BB', CC' and DD' are concurrent.

12. The special case

An important corollary is:

8. *If there exist three distinct points A, B, C such that $C = (A, B)/C$, then, given any three points A', B', C' with $A' \neq B'$, we have $C' = (A', B')/C'$.*

This is evident if $C' = A'$ or $C' = B'$. If C' is distinct from A' and B', there is a projectivity which takes A', B', C' into A, B, C respectively. By the theorem just proved, this projectivity also maps $(A', B')/C'$ on $(A, B)/C$. Since, by hypothesis, this last point coincides with C, we must have

$$C' = (A', B')/C'.$$

Another way of stating this corollary is:

9. *If the diagonal points of any given quadrangle in our plane geometry are collinear, then the diagonal points of every quadrangle in the plane are collinear.*

When this happens we shall say that we are in *the special case*. At a later stage (Ch. VIII, § 6, Th. 3) the special case will be associated with the ground field of coordinates which can be introduced into the plane having characteristic 2. Some modern texts suggest calling such a geometry an *anti-Fano* geometry, on the grounds that one of Fano's postulates in his system of geometry is the non-existence of three such collinear points. But we shall not use this phraseology. He that is not with me is not necessarily against (or anti) me.

13. Further symmetries

To complete the relationship between the pairs A, B and C, D, we first find it convenient to define $(A, B)/C$ when $A = B$. The definition varies with the circumstances. If we are in the special case, we allow any point of the line to be $D = (A, A)/C$. If we are not in the special case we define $(A, A)/C$ to be A when $C \neq A$, and to be any point of the line when $C = A$.

We now prove:

10. *The harmonic relation is not only symmetric in A, B and C, D, but also in the pairs (A, B) and (C, D).*

In other words, we prove that if $D = (A, B)/C$, then $A = (C, D)/B$.

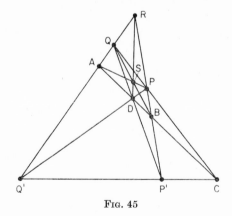

Fig. 45

It may be seen at once that this follows from the definition of harmonic conjugate, with the above convention, if the points A, B, C, D are not all distinct. We need only consider the case, therefore, in which A, B, C, D are four distinct points on l.

With the notation of Fig. 41 let PD meet RA in Q', and QD meet RB in P'. The lines RD, AP, BQ pass through S, so that the sides of the triangles RAB, DPQ must intersect in collinear points. Therefore $P'Q'$ passes through C.

To construct $(C,D)/B$, we draw the lines DP', CP and BPP' through D, C and B, forming the triangle $PP'Q$. The lines DP and CP' meet in Q', and QQ' meets l in the required point, which is therefore A. This proves the theorem.

We may now describe (A,B) and (C,D) as *harmonically conjugate pairs*. The harmonic property is not of much interest in the special case, but it is of fundamental importance in all other cases.

If we are not in the special case we cannot extend Theorem 1 and find a projectivity which relates *four* distinct points A, B, C, D of one range to any four distinct points A', B', C', D' of another. For if $D = (A,B)/C$, but $D' \neq (A',B')/C'$, the existence of such a projectivity would contradict Theorem 7.

14. The dual aspect

Now what about the *dual* aspect of harmonic conjugacy? If we transcribe the construction for $D = (A,B)/C$, we have the following, the construction taking place in the plane π:

Through a point L take two distinct lines a and b. If c is any line through L we construct a new line d through L (see Fig. 46).

Take three points A, B, C lying respectively on a, b, c and distinct from L, and not collinear. Since at least three distinct points lie on every line in the plane π, it is possible to choose A, B, C to satisfy these conditions. Let the join of B and C be p, the join of C and A be q, and let the join AB be the line r. Then a cannot coincide with p, nor b with q. Since a, b, p, q are coplanar lines, and not collinear, there is a line s joining the intersections of a and p and of b and q. Then s must be distinct from r, since b is distinct from a. The point of intersection of r and s has a unique join d to L. This is the line we seek.

It is clear that the diagram (Fig. 46) is essentially the same as Fig. 41. If we call two pairs of points (A,B) and (C,D) which are harmonically conjugate pairs a *harmonic range* and the pairs of lines (a,b) and (c,d) a *harmonic pencil*, then we see that a harmonic pencil is obtained by joining any point not on a line l to the four points of a harmonic range on l, and, dually, any line not through the vertex of a harmonic pencil cuts the four lines of the pencil in the points of a harmonic range.

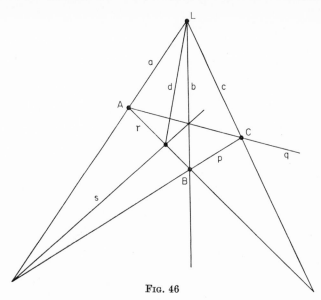

FIG. 46

We can now retrace our steps and investigate the notion of projective ranges from the dual point of view. Beginning with the fundamental notion of *perspective*, two ranges are in perspective if they are both sections of the same pencil of lines. Two pencils of lines can be said to be in perspective if they both project the same range of points. Phrased somewhat differently, we can say:

Two *ranges* $(P, Q, R, ...)$, $(P', Q', R', ...)$ are *perspective* if the joins of corresponding points $PP', QQ', RR', ...$ all pass through a point O.

Two *pencils* $(p, q, r, ...)$, $(p', q', r', ...)$ are *perspective* if the intersections of corresponding lines $pp', qq', rr', ...$ all lie on a line o.

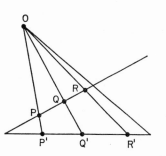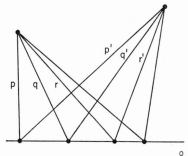

FIG. 47

Two pencils are said to be *projective* if one can be obtained from the other by a finite sequence of perspectivities. The theorems we have proved all have their duals, the proofs being the duals of those already given. Besides the propositions of incidence, the only postulates we have used imply their own duals. We assumed that at least three points lie on every line, which implies that at least three lines pass through every point and we also assumed Desargues' theorem, which we saw involves the dual Desargues theorem (Ch. II, Th. 2).

The *quadrangle* is formed by four points in a plane, no three of which are collinear. The dual construct, the *quadrilateral*, is formed by four lines in a plane, no three of which are concurrent.

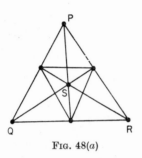

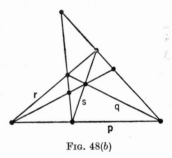

Fig. 48(a)   Fig. 48(b)

Corresponding to the *diagonal points* of the quadrangle we have the *diagonal lines* of the quadrilateral. Our harmonic construction tells us that:

11. *The two sides of the diagonal triangle of a quadrangle which meet in any diagonal point are harmonic with respect to the two sides of the quadrangle which meet in that point.*

12. *The two vertices of the diagonal triangle of a quadrilateral which lie on any diagonal line are harmonic with respect to the two vertices of the quadrilateral which lie on that line.*

Exercises

1. If a, b, c, d and a, b', c', d' are lines of two distinct pencils, and

$$a = (c, d)/b = (c', d')/b',$$

show that the points bb', cc' and dd' are collinear.

2. Let ABC be a given triangle and O a given point of the plane which does not lie on the sides of ABC. Let $AO \cap BC = L$, $BO \cap CA = M$ and $CO \cap AB = N$, and let $MN \cap BC = U$, $NL \cap CA = V$ and $LM \cap AB = W$. Using the result of § 11, **Ex. 1**, prove that CB, MN and VW are concurrent, and deduce that U, V, W are collinear.

3. Calling the line UVW of **Ex.** 2 above the *polar line* of O with respect to the triangle ABC, show that if O, O' are two points whose join passes through A, then the polar lines of O and O' meet on BC.

15. A property of quadrangles

As we are discussing quadrangles, we may mention two properties which merely depend on Desargues' theorem, and therefore could have come in at an earlier stage (see Fig. 49).

13. *If ABC is the diagonal triangle of a quadrangle $PQRS$, the three points given by the intersections of BC and QR, CA and RP and AB and PQ are collinear.*

The two triangles ABC and PQR are perspective from the point S, so that the result follows from Desargues' theorem.

As a corollary, we have:

14. *Given the diagonal triangle and one vertex of a quadrangle, the remaining three vertices may be constructed by joins of points and intersection of lines.*

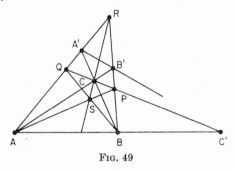

Fig. 49

In fact, given the diagonal triangle ABC and vertex P, we construct in turn:

B' as the intersection of CA and BP, C' as the intersection of AB and CP, A' as the intersection of BC and $B'C'$.

We then have R as the intersection of BP and AA', Q as the intersection of CP and AA', and finally S as the intersection of AP and BQ.

The above theorems have duals, of course, which the reader should write down.

16. A theorem on perspectivities

A theorem which is of fundamental importance in the section on involutions (Ch. IV, Th. 2) is the following:

15. *If A, A', B, B' are any four collinear points, then*

$$(A, A', B, B') \barwedge (A', A, B', B).$$

We show, in fact, that it is possible, by a sequence of three perspectivities, to interchange pairs amongst any four collinear points.

Draw any triangle TUP whose sides UP, PT and TU pass through A, B and B' respectively. Two further points are determined in the figure (Fig. 50), S as the intersection of $A'P$ and TU, and V as the intersection of AS and BP. We now have the relations

$$(A, A', B, B') \overset{P}{\barwedge} (U, S, T, B') \overset{A}{\barwedge} (P, V, T, B) \overset{S}{\barwedge} (A', A, B', B),$$

which proves the theorem.

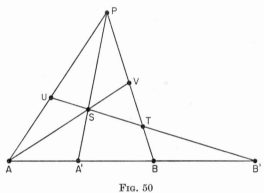

FIG. 50

17. Pappus and projectivities

We conclude this chapter with a fundamental theorem for which our previous detailed work on perspectivities has been an essential preparation. We have seen (§ 3, Th. 1) that it is possible to establish a projectivity between two ranges so that three distinct points of the one range correspond to three distinct points of the other. On the other hand, if we are given four points A, B, C, D of one range, and four points A', B', C', D' of the other, there may be no projectivity in which A, B, C, D correspond, respectively, to A', B', C' and D'. We now prove our fundamental theorem:

16. *A necessary and sufficient condition that a projectivity between two ranges be uniquely determined by the assignment of three pairs of corresponding points is that Pappus' theorem be true.*

1. *Necessity.* Suppose that a projectivity is uniquely determined when three pairs of corresponding points are given.

Let ABC, $A'B'C'$ be two triads of points on two lines l and l' which intersect at O. Let $B'C, BC'$ meet at P, $CA', C'A$ meet in Q, and $A'B, AB'$ at R.

(a) If the triads are in perspective from a point V, then clearly the lines OP, OQ and OR all coincide with the harmonic conjugate of OV with respect to l and l'. Hence P, Q and R are collinear, and Pappus' theorem is true without any further condition (see Fig. 51).

If the triads are not given as being in perspective, but we are told that the line joining two of the points P, Q and R, say the line QR, passes through O, we easily deduce that the triads must be in

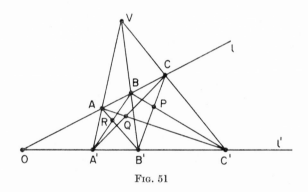

Fig. 51

perspective, so that we are in the case already considered. For if BB' meets AA' in V, then OV is the harmonic conjugate of OR with respect to l and l'. If CC' meets AA' in V', then OV' is the harmonic conjugate of OQ with respect to l and l'. Hence OV coincides with OV', and therefore $V = V'$, the triads are in perspective, and P, Q, R are collinear.

(b) If the triads are not in perspective, we use the hypothesis that a projectivity is determined by the assignment of three corresponding pairs of points to deduce Pappus' theorem.

Let QR meet l in L, and l' in M'. Then the points L, M' and O are all distinct, by what we have just proved. Let AA' meet QR in S. We denote the line $LM'QR$ by l^*.

By hypothesis there is a unique projectivity between the ranges on l and l' in which A, B, C correspond, respectively, to A', B', C'.

This projectivity may therefore be defined by the perspectivities

$$(A, B, C, \ldots) \underset{\overline{\wedge}}{\overset{A'}{}} (S, R, Q, \ldots) \underset{\overline{\wedge}}{\overset{A}{}} (A', B', C', \ldots),$$

for this is a projectivity, being the result of two perspectivities, and such a projectivity, by hypothesis, is unique.

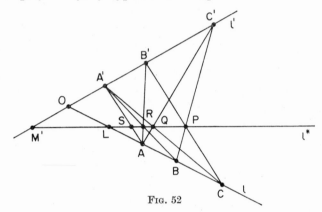

Fig. 52

Now, regarding O as a point of l, there is a unique point of l' corresponding to it in the range on l'. Passing from l to l' via l^* by the above perspectivities, O becomes M', and then M'. Similarly, the point L of l corresponds to O of l'. Since, by hypothesis, the projectivity is uniquely determined by the pairs A, A', B, B' and C, C', the points L, M' are uniquely determined by the projectivity. The line l^* is therefore uniquely determined by the projectivity, and this line contains the points Q and R.

Now, if we choose B and B' as centres of perspective, we find that the line RP cuts l in the point L and l' in the point M'. That is, R and P also lie on l^*. Hence P, Q and R are collinear, and Pappus' theorem is true.

18. Projective ranges perspective

2. *Sufficiency.* We now suppose that Pappus' theorem is true. Before proving our theorem we need a lemma which, together with its dual, will be very useful to us later on.

LEMMA 1. *If l, l' are distinct lines intersecting in O, and if ranges $(P, Q, R, O, \ldots)$ $(P', Q', R', O', \ldots)$ on l and l' are projectively related so that O on l corresponds to O on l', then the ranges are in perspective.*

It is evident that if the ranges *are* in perspective the point O on l corresponds to the point O on l'. Now, we can pass from the range on l to that on l' by, at most, two perspectivities (§ 4, Th. 2). There is nothing to prove if we can pass from one range to the other by a *single* perspectivity. Let there be two then, and denote the intermediary line by $l*$ (see Fig. 53).

If $l*$ passes through O, the ranges on l and l' are in perspective (§ 5, Th. 3). We suppose, then, that $l*$ meets l in P, the line l' in Q',

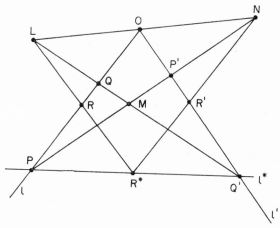

Fig. 53

and that P, Q' and O are distinct points. We pass from the range on l to a range on $l*$ by a perspectivity with vertex L, and then from the range on $l*$ to that on l' by a perspectivity, vertex N. It is easily verified that P and Q' do not correspond in the projectivity. If $L = N$, the ranges on l and l' are in perspective, vertex $L = N$. If $L \neq N$, the line LN must pass through O, since O on l corresponds to O on l'. Let LQ' meet l in Q, let NP meet l' in P', and let LQ' meet NP in M. If R is any other point of l, and R' the corresponding point of the range on l', then LR and NR' must meet in a point $R*$ of $l*$. Applying Pappus' theorem to the triads LON and $PR*Q'$ we see that RR' passes through M. Since R and R' are any pair of corresponding points, it follows that the ranges are in perspective from M, and the lemma is proved.

19. Sufficiency of Pappus

We now return to our main theorem. Assuming Pappus' theorem, we wish to prove that a projectivity between two ranges is uniquely determined by the assignment of three pairs of corresponding points.

Let $(P, Q, R, \ldots)$ and $(P', Q', R', \ldots)$ be ranges on two distinct lines l and l', and suppose that there are *two* projectivities Π and Π' between the ranges which make P, Q and R correspond to P', Q' and R' respectively. If a pair of corresponding points, say P and P', coincide at the intersection of l and l', then, by the lemma just proved, Π and Π' are both perspectivities with the intersection of QQ' and RR' as vertex of perspective. In this case we must have $\Pi = \Pi'$. Since the three pairs of corresponding points are assumed to be distinct pairs, we can select points on l and l', say Q and R', which are both distinct from the possible intersection of l and l', and do not correspond. We can now pass from the range on l to the range on l' by two perspectivities in which QR' is the intermediary line l^* for both projectivities Π and Π' (§ 6, Th. 4).

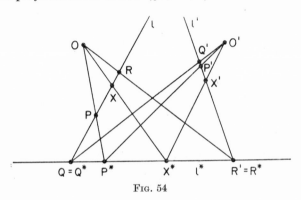

Fig. 54

Let the vertices of perspective for Π be O and O'. If X is any other point of l, and X' the point on l' corresponding to X in Π, then

$$(P, Q, R, X) \underset{\overline{\wedge}}{\overset{O}{=}} (P^*, Q^*, R^*, X^*) \underset{\overline{\wedge}}{\overset{O'}{=}} (P', Q', R', X'),$$

where $Q^* = Q$ and $R^* = R'$.

Now let $\bar{X}$ be the point of l' corresponding to X in Π', and let $O'\bar{X}$ meet l^* in $\bar{X}^*$. Then

$$(P^*, Q^*, R^*, \bar{X}^*) \underset{\overline{\wedge}}{\overset{O'}{=}} (P', Q', R', \bar{X}) \overline{\wedge} (P, Q, R, X) \quad \text{(in } \Pi'\text{)}.$$

Since $Q^* = Q$, the ranges $(P^*, Q^*, R^*, \bar{X}^*)$ and (P, Q, R, X), by the lemma above, must be in perspective. The vertex must be O. Hence O, X and $\bar{X}^*$ are collinear points. That is, $\bar{X}^* = X^*$, and therefore $X' = \bar{X}$, and hence $\Pi = \Pi'$.

If the ranges $(P, Q, R, \ldots)$ and $(P', Q', R', \ldots)$ are on the same line l, we project the second range on to a line l', obtaining a range $(P'', Q'', R'', \ldots)$. If there were two distinct projectivities from $(P, Q, R, \ldots)$ to $(P', Q', R', \ldots)$ there would be two distinct projectivities from $(P, Q, R, \ldots)$ to $(P'', Q'', R'', \ldots)$ and we have just shown that this is not so. This concludes the proof of Theorem 16.

The way is now clear to the most characteristic developments of our subject. We reserve most of the new subject matter for another chapter, but we state here the dual of the lemma above, and then apply this dual theorem to a promised deduction of Desargues' theorem from Pappus' theorem (Ch. II, § 13).

LEMMA 2. *If L and L' are distinct points whose join is o, and if pencils $(p, q, r, o, \ldots)$, $(p', q', r', o, \ldots)$ with vertices L and L' are projectively related so that the line o through L corresponds to the line o through L', then the pencils are in perspective.*

This means, of course, that corresponding lines in the two pencils intersect in the points of a line.

20. Desargues' theorem via Pappus

We now give the proof of Desargues' theorem promised at the end of Chapter II. As we are assuming Pappus' theorem, we may assume any consequences of that theorem.

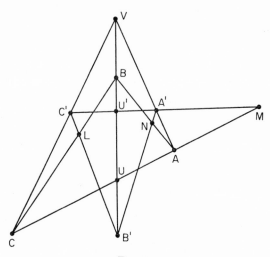

FIG. 55

The triads ABC and $A'B'C'$ are in perspective from V, and corresponding sides BC and $B'C'$, CA and $C'A'$, and AB and $A'B'$ meet in L, M and N respectively. We want to prove that L, M and N are collinear. Let BB' meet AC in U and $A'C'$ in U'.

It is sufficient to show that

$$B'(B, N, L, M) \barwedge B(B', N, L, M),$$

for then we shall have two projective pencils with a common ray, and corresponding lines in the pencil intersect at N, L and M. Taking sections of the two pencils by the lines $A'C'$ and AC respectively, this relationship is true if and only if

$$(U', A', C', M) \barwedge (U, A, C, M).$$

But these two ranges are in perspective from V. Hence L, M, N are collinear.

21. Breakdown of the shorter proof

We saw in Chapter II, § 10, that care has to be exercised in the application of the Pappus theorem, in order to ensure that such applications are meaningful. We must exercise similar care in the application of the theorem, used above in § 20, that *two projective pencils with a common ray are perspective, the intersections of corresponding rays being three collinear points.* If the projective pencils have *two* common rays, one of the three points which we wish to prove collinear is not uniquely defined, and the theorem has no meaningful application.

The proof of the Desargues theorem given above in § 20 breaks down if any one of the points L, M or N lies on BB'. With our assumption (see Ch. II, § 11) that the seven points V, A, B, C, A', B', C' are distinct, that the three lines VAA', VBB' and VCC' are distinct, and that each triad, ABC, $A'B'C'$, is a proper triad, we now show that neither L nor N can lie on BB'.

Since $L = BC \cap B'C'$, if $L \in BB'$ this implies that B, B' and C are collinear, and also that B, B' and C' are collinear, so that $BC = B'C'$. Since $VBB' \neq VCC'$, this is impossible. Similarly, if $N = AB \cap A'B'$ lies on BB', we should have B, B' and A collinear, and also B, B' and A' collinear, giving $VAA' = VBB'$, which is also ruled out.

But it is possible for M to lie on BB', and we now show that this is equivalent to the specialization $B' \in CA$ of the Desargues configuration. If we choose A as centre of perspective, the triangles

BCV and NMA' are in perspective from A, and corresponding sides intersect at the collinear points L, C', B'. We can rename the points

$$A, \quad B, C, V, \quad N, M, A', \quad L, C', B'$$
$$V, \quad A, B, C, \quad A', B', C', \quad N, L, M$$

and we now see that $M \in VB = VBB'$ in the first row is equivalent to $B' \in CA$ in the second row.

The specialization $B' \in CA$ is one we are already familiar with from the proof of the Desargues theorem via Pappus given in Chapter II, §11 onwards. It is clear that there is no proof of the Desargues theorem via Pappus which is independent of the possible specializations of the configuration.

Exercise

1. Show that if $L \in AA'$ and $M \in BB'$ in the Desargues configuration, then $N \in CC'$ only if we are in the special case, with the diagonal points of the quadrangle $BLAM$ collinear.

CHAPTER IV

THE CROSS-AXIS, UNITED POINTS AND INVOLUTIONS

1. The cross-axis of a projectivity

From now on we shall assume Pappus' theorem to be true, and we may therefore use the fundamental theorem that a projectivity between the points of two lines (which may coincide) is uniquely determined by the assignment of three pairs of corresponding points (Ch. III, §17, Th. 16).

1. *If* $(A, B, C, ..., X) \barwedge (A', B', C', ..., X')$, *and corresponding points lie on two distinct lines, then the intersections of cross-joins such as* AX' *and* $A'X$ *lie on a line.*

This is called the *cross-axis* of the correspondence between the two lines.

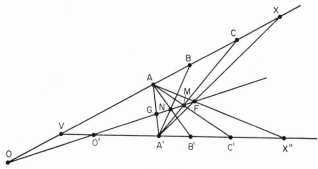

FIG. 56

Let AB' and $A'B$ meet in N, and $A'C$ and AC' meet in M. Let $A'X$ meet the line MN in F, and let AF meet the line $B'C'$ in X''. Then if AA' meets the line MN in G, we have the relations

$$(A, B, C, X) \overset{A'}{\barwedge} (G, N, M, F) \overset{A}{\barwedge} (A', B', C', X'').$$

But since the projectivity is uniquely determined, the points X' and X'' must coincide. Hence the intersection of AX' and $A'X$ lies on a fixed line.

This theorem gives us an effective method of constructing pairs of corresponding points on two projective ranges when three pairs of corresponding points are assigned. The cross-axis is the Pappus line obtained from the cross-joins of the corresponding triads ABC and $A'B'C'$.

If the two ranges intersect at the point V, then V corresponds to a point on the second range if it is regarded as a point on the first range, and to a point on the first range if it is regarded as a point on the second range. If the points corresponding to V be,

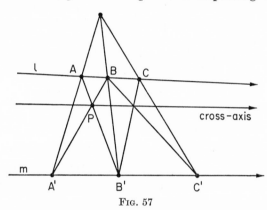

FIG. 57

respectively, O' and O, then it is clear that the cross-axis is the line OO'. The points O and O' coincide with V when the ranges $(A, B, C, ...)$ and $(A', B', C', ...)$ are in perspective. In that case the cross-axis is the harmonic conjugate of the line joining the centre of perspective to V with respect to the two ranges. This suggests (see Fig. 57) another solution to the first problem of Chapter I, §9, illustrated in Fig. 4.

The reader should write down the dual theorem corresponding to Theorem 1 above.

2. United points of a projectivity

We now turn to projective ranges on the same line. If we denote the projective transformation by which a point P' on the line arises from a point P by the symbol Π, so that $\Pi(P) = P'$, then a point U on the line which is such that $\Pi(U) = U$ is called an *invariant*, *united*, *double* or *fixed point* of the projective transformation Π.

The *inverse* transformation which maps P' on P is denoted by Π^{-1}. Since, if

$$\Pi(U) = U, \quad \text{then} \quad U = \Pi^{-1}(U),$$

we see that a united point of the direct transformation is also a
united point of the inverse transformation.

The only projective transformations with *three* united points are
the identity transformations, $\Pi(P) = P$, for which every point on the
line is a united point. This follows from the theorem that Π is
uniquely determined by the assignment of three pairs of corresponding points. The identity transformation is a projective
transformation, and since this maps each of the three given united
points on itself, it must be the one we are looking for.

Projective transformations with two united points and with only
one united point do exist, however, and are easily constructed.

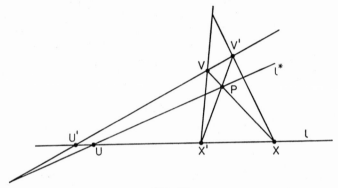

FIG. 58

V and V' are given points, l^* a given line, and l the line on which
we are considering a projective transformation. If X is any point
on l, let VX meet l^* in P, and let $V'P$ meet l in X'. Then

$$(X')\overline{\wedge}(X),$$

being the product of two perspectivities. If VV' meets l in U', and l^*
meets l in U, the points U and U' are united points, being unchanged
under the projective transformation just described. If P is at U,
then $X = U$ and also $X' = U$. If P is at the point where l^* meets
VV', then $X = U'$ and also $X' = U'$.

Hence we have a projectivity with two united points. If we take
the case in which the line VV' meets l^* and l at a point U, then U
is the only united point of the projectivity between points X and X'.
For if $X = X'$, this can only be at U (see Fig. 59).

The two projective transformations we have just considered are
each the product of *two* perspectivities, and are therefore not the

most general projectivity between the points of a line. We saw in
Ch. III, §7, Corollary, Theorem 2 that *three* perspectivities may be
necessary to produce a given projectivity between the points of a
line. This warning is necessary lest the reader think that all

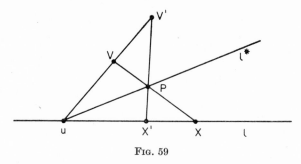

FIG. 59

projectivities on a line have at least one united point. In a given
geometry there may be none. Once coordinates have been introduced
it will be possible to discuss this matter more fully (Ch. VII, §12).

3. The method of false positions

If we are merely given three pairs of corresponding points on a
line, the projectivity between points of the line in which these pairs
are mates is uniquely determined, and may have united points in
the geometry, but, so far, we have not discussed any method of
finding them. There is a class of problem, first introduced by Poncelet,
whose solution depends on the existence and determination of such
united points. A typical example is the following (see Fig. 60):

*To describe a quadrilateral such that its four sides pass through given
points and its four vertices lie on given lines.*

Let A, B, C and D be the four fixed points, and l_1, l_2, l_3 and l_4 the
four fixed lines. Through A draw any line cutting l_1, l_2 at P_1, P_2.
Join BP_2 and produce it to cut l_3 at P_3; join CP_3 and produce it to
cut l_4 at P_4; join DP_4 and produce it to cut l_1 at P'. Then

$$(P_1, \ldots) \barwedge A(P_1, \ldots) \barwedge (P_2, \ldots) \barwedge B(P_2, \ldots)$$

$$\barwedge (P_3, \ldots) \barwedge C(P_3, \ldots) \barwedge (P_4, \ldots)$$

$$\barwedge D(P_4, \ldots) \barwedge (P', \ldots).$$

Therefore
$$(P_1, \ldots) \barwedge (P', \ldots)$$

on the line l_1.

Now, if we can find the united points U and U' of this projective correspondence on l_1, then either AU or AU' may be taken as a side of the required quadrilateral, and the other sides are then at once determined. In our construction the point P' will then

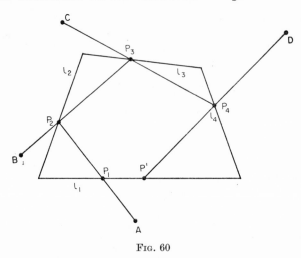

Fig. 60

coincide with P_1, and the quadrilateral will *close up*. Again, if the quadrilateral does close up, the points P_1 and P' must coincide, and must therefore be united points of the projective correspondence.

Hence there are at most two solutions of the given problem. We shall see later (Ch. IX, § 10) how the united points can be found if we start with any three pairs of corresponding points. The solution necessarily involves the use of a conic.

Since the production of three pairs of corresponding points usually involves the construction of three quadrilaterals which do not close up, and are therefore not solutions of the problem, the method is often called "the method of false positions". Three constructions which are false, in that they do not solve the problem, provide the material for a solution of the problem.

Exercise

1. A ray of light starts from a given source O, is reflected from a given line l, with which it is incident at a point P, and meets a distinct line m at Q. Show that the ranges (P) and (Q) are in perspective.

If the ray starting at O is reflected in succession by three given lines l, m and n, show how to determine the initial path if the final reflected ray is parallel to the initial incident ray.

4. Periodic projectivities

Suppose that a given projectivity on a line relates X to X', X' to X'', and so on, so that

$$(X, X', X'', ..., X^{(n-1)}) \barwedge (X', X'', X''', ..., X^{(n)}).$$

If $X^{(n)}$ coincides with X for three positions of X on the line, it will do so for all positions of X on the line. This follows from the fact that if the original projectivity mapping X on X' is denoted by Π, then the mapping of X on $X^{(n)}$ is also a projectivity, and is represented by Π^n. If a projectivity has three united points, it is the identity.

If Π^n is the identity, the projectivity Π is said to be *periodic*, and the smallest n for which this happens is called *the period*.

The identity is of period 1. If we take two fixed points U and U' on a line, and let X' be the harmonic conjugate of X with respect to U and U', then X' is projectively related to X, and if $\Pi(X) = X'$, we know that $\Pi(X') = X$. Hence this projectivity is of period 2.

If A, B, C are three points on a line, we can set up a projectivity in which $(A, B, C) \barwedge (B, C, A)$. This projectivity is of period 3, since if applied thrice to A, B and C respectively it produces A, B and C respectively.

5. Involutions

We are especially interested in projectivities of period 2. These are called *involutions*, and have remarkable properties.

2. *A projectivity that interchanges two points on a line is necessarily an involution.*

In other words, if $\Pi(A) = A'$ and $\Pi(A') = A$ for any pair of points A, A' on a line, then if X is any other point, and $\Pi(X) = X'$, then $\Pi(X') = X$.

To prove this we note that, by the fundamental theorem, Π is uniquely determined as the projectivity which maps (A, A', X) on (A', A, X'). If X' is mapped on X'', we should have

$$(A, A', X, X') \barwedge (A', A, X', X'').$$

But we know, by Ch. III, §16, Theorem 15, that

$$(A, A', X, X') \barwedge (A', A, X', X).$$

It follows that X and X'' are the same point, and the projectivity is an involution.

Corollary. An involution is determined by any two of its pairs.

If (AA') and (BB') are paired in an involution, we may denote the involution $(A, A', B, B') \barwedge (A', A, B', B)$ by the symbol

$$(AA')(BB').$$

Either pair may be replaced by a united point repeated. The involution
$$(A, A', U) \barwedge (A', A, U)$$

is denoted by $(AA')(UU)$.

We have already noted that an involution arises if we find the harmonic conjugate of a point with respect to two given fixed points. Such an involution is not at all special, as we see from the following theorem:

3. *If an involution has one united point, it has another, and the involution is just the correspondence between harmonic conjugates with respect to these points.*

Consider the involution $(AA')(UU)$, and let U' be the harmonic conjugate of U with respect to A and A'. Then U' is also the harmonic conjugate of U with respect to A' and A. But the involution, being a projectivity, preserves the harmonic relation (Ch. III, §11, Th. 7). Hence U' is a second invariant point, distinct from U.†

If another pair XX' is used instead of AA', we still obtain the same harmonic conjugate U', since otherwise the involution would have three united points.

An involution can be determined by its two united points U and U', and is then denoted by the symbol $(UU)(U'U')$.

Of course, an involution may have no united points. This will become clearer when coordinates are introduced (Ch. VII, §12).

6. Involutions and projectivities

Involutions are the bricks from which projectivities on a line may be constructed. In fact, only two bricks are necessary, and we have the theorem:

4. *Any projectivity between the points of a line may be expressed as the product of two involutions.*

Let the given projectivity be denoted by Π, and suppose that A is not a united point of Π, and that $\Pi(A) = A'$, and that $\Pi(A') = A''$.

---

† We are assuming, of course, that we do not have the special case of Ch. III, § 12, Th. 9 to contend with.

We consider the involution I which is defined by the symbol $(AA'')(A'A')$. Then the projectivity $I\Pi$ operating on A produces the point A', since $\Pi(A) = A'$, and $I(A') = A'$, and the same projectivity operating on A' produces the point A, since $\Pi(A') = A''$, and $I(A'') = A$.

Hence the projectivity denoted by $I\Pi$ must be an involution, which we denote by J. But if $I\Pi = J$, then $I^2\Pi = IJ$, and since I is an involution, the symbol I^2 represents the identity, and we finally have

$$\Pi = IJ,$$

which shows the projectivity Π expressed as the product of two involutions.

Exercise

1. Two projectivities Π_1 and Π_2 are said to commute if

$$\Pi_1(\Pi_2(P)) = \Pi_2(\Pi_1(P))$$

for all points P. Prove that if Π_1 and Π_2 are both involutions, they commute if and only if $\Pi_1\Pi_2$ is also an involution.

If U and V are the united points of the involution Π_1, and E and F are the united points of the involution Π_2 ($\neq \Pi_1$), prove that a necessary and sufficient condition that Π_1 and Π_2 commute is that U, V and E, F are pairs in a harmonic range.

7. Criteria for involutions

It is very useful to have a criterion by which we can judge whether three given pairs of points on a line are in involution.

5. *A necessary and sufficient condition for three pairs of points AA', BB' and CC' to belong to an involution is $(A, B, C, C') \barwedge (A', B', C', C)$.*

If C, C' is a pair of the involution $(AA')(BB')$, the relation follows because the points A, B, C and C' are mapped on the points A', B', C' and C respectively. So the condition is necessary.

It is also sufficient, since it shows that in the unique projectivity which maps A, B and C on A', B' and C' respectively, the point C' is mapped on C. The projectivity is therefore an involution (§5, Th. 2).

We may have $A = A'$, or $B = B'$, but the nature of the proof requires C and C' to be distinct points.

Since in a projectivity we may interchange pairs amongst four collinear points, the above theorem may also be written in the form:

6. *A necessary and sufficient condition for three pairs of points AA', BB' and CC' to belong to an involution is $(A, B, C, C') \barwedge (B', A', C, C')$.*

Noting that in this enunciation C and C' are unchanged in position, we may change the notation, and say that a necessary and sufficient condition for the pair of points M and N to belong to the involution $(AA')(BB')$ is

$$(M, N, A, B) \overline{\wedge} (M, N, B', A').$$

Since the involution $(AA')(BB')$ is the same as the involution $(AA')(B'B)$, the relation $(M, N, A, B) \overline{\wedge} (M, N, B', A')$ is equivalent to the relation $(M, N, A, B') \overline{\wedge} (M, N, B, A')$, since either one may be deduced from the other.

Changing the notation once again, this result is more easily remembered in the form:

The relation $(M, N, P, Q) \overline{\wedge} (M, N, P,'Q')$ *is equivalent to the relation* $(M, N, P, P') \overline{\wedge} (M, N, Q, Q')$.

The reader should now take this form of the theorem, and prove it, without any change of notation, by repeating the initial argument, using the theory of involutions.

Exercise

1. Prove that the pencils joining any point on the cross-axis of two projective ranges to corresponding points of the ranges are in involution.

Let us now suppose that the two involutions $(PP'')(QQ'')$ and $(P'P'')(Q'Q'')$ share a common pair of points M, N, so that the pair M, N belongs both to the first and to the second involution. We have just seen that a necessary and sufficient condition for M, N to belong to the first involution is

$$(M, N, P, Q) \overline{\wedge} (M, N, Q'', P'').$$

Similarly, a necessary and sufficient condition for M, N to belong to the second involution is

$$(M, N, Q'', P'') \overline{\wedge} (M, N, P', Q').$$

Since the pair M, N is in both involutions, we deduce that

$$(M, N, P, Q) \overline{\wedge} (M, N, P', Q').$$

But this is a necessary and sufficient condition for the pair M, N to belong to the involution $(PQ')(QP')$. We therefore have the theorem:

7. *If* M, N *is a pair of each of the involutions* $(PP'')(QQ'')$ *and* $(P'P'')(Q'Q'')$, *then it is also a pair of the involution* $(PQ')(QP')$. †

---

† We shall see later (Ch. IX, § 11) that this is equivalent to Pascal's theorem for six points on a conic.

8. Quadrangular sets

We can now easily prove the following theorem:

8. *The three pairs of opposite sides of a quadrangle meet any line (not through a vertex) in three pairs of points in involution.*

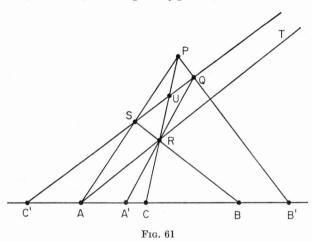

FIG. 61

Let the quadrangle be formed by the points P, Q, R and S. Let PR and QS meet in U, and let a line meet PS in A, QR in A', RS in B, PQ in B', PR in C and QS in C'. Let AR meet QS in T. Then we have the relations:

$$(A, B, C, C') \overline{\underset{\overline{\wedge}}{\underset{=}{R}}} (T, S, U, C') \overline{\underset{\overline{\wedge}}{\underset{=}{A}}} (R, P, U, C) \overline{\underset{\overline{\wedge}}{\underset{=}{Q}}} (A', B', C', C).$$

We deduce that

$$(A, B, C, C') \overline{\wedge} (A', B', C', C).$$

It follows that the pairs (A, A'), (B, B') and (C, C') are in involution.

We note that this proof makes use of the fundamental theorem. Let us suppose that the points A, A' and B, B' are given. If we take any point C on the line AB distinct from these four points, we can easily construct a quadrangle with vertices P, Q, R and S whose opposite sides pass through A and A', B and B'. If we carry out the construction correctly, one of the two remaining sides can be made to pass through C. All we have to do, in fact, is to draw any line through C distinct from the line AB. On it choose any two points P and R distinct from each other and C. Then the intersection of BR and AP gives S, and the intersection of $A'R$ and $B'P$ gives Q.

Now, given A, A', B, B' and C, the theorem we have just proved tells us that however we construct the quadrangle with vertices P, Q, R and S, the point C' in which QS meets AB is a fixed point.

The theorem in this form was known to Pappus. We can prove a weaker form of it by merely assuming Desargues' theorem. The theorem is:

9. *If two quadrangles P, Q, R, S and P', Q', R', S' correspond, P to P', Q to Q', R to R' and S to S' in such a way that five of the pairs of corresponding sides intersect in points of a line l, then the sixth pair of corresponding sides will also intersect in a point of l.*

We leave the proof of this to the reader.

The set of points A, A', B, B', C, C' is naturally called a *quadrangular set* of points.

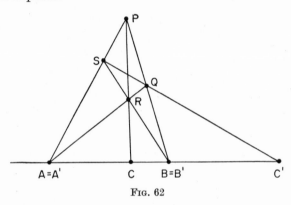

FIG. 62

If we consider the case when $A = A'$ and $B = B'$, we still have the involution property, but now A and B are united points, and we see that we are back at the construction for harmonic conjugates (Ch. III, § 8, Fig. 41).

All the theorems above have duals. In particular, the notion of an *involution pencil* of lines through a point is of great importance, and we have the dual theorem:

10. *The join of the three pairs of opposite vertices of a quadrilateral to any point (not on a side) gives three pairs of lines in involution.*

Exercise

1. The four given points A, B, Q, V lie on a line, and a given line through V meets a given line through Q at O. The point X is variable on OV, and AX meets QO at P, and BP meets QX at J. Prove that J moves on a fixed line through O.

CHAPTER V

COLLINEATIONS IN PROJECTIVE PLANES

1. Recapitulation of axioms

In the first chapter of this book we investigated the effect of *conical projection* on the points and lines of a plane. We found that if the points P and the lines l of a plane π are projected from a vertex V on to a plane π', the points P are mapped on points P', and the lines l are mapped on lines l' in π'. Incidence properties are preserved, and $P' \in l'$ if and only if $P \in l$.

When the planes π and π' became coincident, we had a transformation, or mapping, of the plane π on to itself, in which points are mapped on points, lines on lines, and incidence properties are preserved. Such a mapping is called a *collineation*.

It will be observed that we have not mentioned the possibility that some points P in π have no corresponding P'. In fact, we now adopt the projective point of view, in which no line in π has special significance. We formally define our plane, and obtain a number of fundamental properties before considering the properties of collineations of a projective plane.

Axioms.

A projective plane is a set of points, with certain subsets† called lines, satisfying the following axioms:

    I. *Any two distinct points are contained in one and only one line.*

    II. *Any two distinct lines have in common one and only one point.*

    III. *There exist at least four points, no three of which are contained in one line.*

The first two axioms are the axioms of incidence. We call the unique line containing the distinct points A and B *the line joining A and B*, and denote it by AB. The unique point contained in two distinct lines l and m is called the *intersection* of l and m, and denoted by $l \cap m$.

---

† More formally, lines and points are distinct entities, with a possible relation of incidence between them. For our purposes, a line is defined as the subset of points with which it is incident.

A more consistent notation for the line AB would be $A \cup B$. Some writers use $A + B$.

Points on the same line are said to be *collinear*. Lines through the same point are said to be *concurrent*. Since lines are defined as sets of points, it is consistent (and convenient) to use the notation $P \in l$ for P *lies on* l, and $P \notin l$ for P *does not lie on* l.

In our discussion of the projective geometry of a plane we are limited to the consequences of the three axioms above.

Exercises

1. From $AB = CD$ and $B \neq C$ prove that $AB = BC$.
2. From $AB \neq AC$ prove that $AB \cap AC = A$.

2. First deductions

We now investigate the consequences of the third axiom. Let P_1, P_2, P_3, P_4 be four points, no three of which are collinear. These are said to form a *quadrangle*. If we consider the lines joining these points taken in pairs, there are six. These six lines are all distinct, and every two intersect in one point. We therefore obtain three further points Q_1, Q_2, Q_3, and the six lines, with the points on them, are

$$l_1 : (P_1 P_2 Q_1), \quad l_2 : (P_1 P_3 Q_2), \quad l_3 : (P_1 P_4 Q_3),$$
$$l_4 : (P_2 P_3 Q_3), \quad l_5 : (P_2 P_4 Q_2), \quad l_6 : (P_3 P_4 Q_1).$$

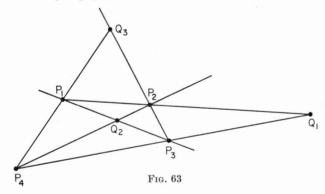

FIG. 63

Exercise

1. Prove that Q_1, Q_2, Q_3 are distinct from the P_i and from each other.

The six lines $l_1, ..., l_6$ already constructed each contain at least three points. We prove that this is true for any line l in the plane. Since the lines l_1, l_2, l_3 all pass through P_1, l will cut these lines in distinct points, if it does not pass through P_1. If l does not contain P_2, it will cut l_4, l_5, l_1 in three distinct points. If l contains both

P_1 and P_2, then it is the line l_1, which contains the three distinct points P_1, P_2, Q_1. Hence:

1. *Every line contains at least three points.*

Corresponding to Axiom III, we have:

2. *There are at least four lines, no three of which are concurrent.*

In fact, the lines l_1, l_2, l_5, l_6 satisfy this condition.

3. Principle of duality

The principle of duality has already been mentioned. It enables us to produce a *Doppelgänger* for every theorem in the projective plane, two theorems for the price of one.

If we interchange the terms "points" and "lines", and replace "contains" by "is contained in", Axioms I and II are interchanged, and Axiom III and Theorem 2 are interchanged. This is really sufficient to establish *the principle of duality*, but more formally we proceed thus:

Let our projective plane π consist of the set of points P_i and the set of lines l_i. Let π^* be a projective plane in which the lines p_i are in one-to-one correspondence with the points P_i of π, and the points L_j are in one-to-one correspondence with the lines l_j of π. Again, if $P_i \in l_j$ in π, we put $L_j \in p_i$ in π^*, where P_i and p_i correspond, as do L_j and l_j. It is clear that π^* satisfies the Axioms I, II, III, and is therefore a projective plane.

We also note that the same procedure applied to π^* leads back to π; that is, $(\pi^*)^* = \pi$.

Now, any statement about a plane π, deduced from the axioms, is also true about the plane π^*. But in π^* the points of π become lines, the lines of π become points, and if $P_i \in l_j$ in π we have $L_j \in p_i$ in π^*. Hence every theorem which is true for π gives rise to a *dual* theorem. This is *the principle of duality*.

Applying this principle to Theorem 1, we have:

3. *Every point in a projective plane is on at least three lines.*

4. Finite projective geometries

There are projective planes which only contain a finite number of points. These are called *finite projective planes*. Their existence will be demonstrated later (§ 12). In the meantime we investigate certain fundamental aspects of such planes.

By Axiom III, a projective plane π contains at least one set of four points P, Q, R, S, no three of which are collinear. Let the line

$RS = l$ contain $n+1$ points, where $n \geqslant 2$ by Theorem 1. We prove that every line in π contains exactly $n+1$ points, and that $n+1$ lines pass through every point.

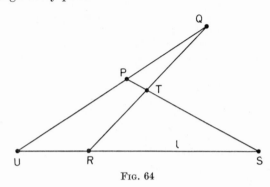

Fig. 64

Let PQ and l meet in U. Then PS and QR meet in a further point T which is not on l and not on PQ. If V is any point not on l, joining V to the $n+1$ points of l gives $n+1$ lines through V. There are no further lines through V, since every line through V must intersect l, and there are only $n+1$ points on l. In particular, there are $n+1$ lines through each of P, Q and T. Now any line m of the plane cannot contain more than two of the points P, Q and T. It is therefore intersected by the $n+1$ lines through one of these points in $n+1$ points, and these are all the points on m, since additional points would give rise to additional lines through one of the points P, Q, T. There are $n+1$ lines through any point V of π, these being obtained by joining the point to the $n+1$ points of any line not containing V.

We have now practically completed the proof of the following theorem:

4. *Let $n \geqslant 2$ be any integer. In a finite projective plane the following properties are equivalent:*

  (1) *One line contains exactly $n+1$ points.*

  (2) *One point is on exactly $n+1$ lines.*

  (3) *Every line contains exactly $n+1$ points.*

  (4) *Every point is on exactly $n+1$ lines.*

  (5) *There are exactly n^2+n+1 points.*

  (6) *There are exactly n^2+n+1 lines.*

To prove (5), let V be any point of π, and let us consider the $n+1$ lines through V. These lines contain all the points of π. Each line contains $n+1$ points, including V. The number of distinct points in π is therefore

$$1+n(n+1) = n^2+n+1.$$

A dual argument gives (6). Hence (1) implies all the remaining properties.

By duality (2) implies the remaining properties. Evidently (3) implies (1), and (4) implies (2). If we begin with (5), then some line has $m+1$ points, where m is an integer, and we conclude that π has $m^2+m+1 = n^2+n+1$ points, whence $m = n$ and (5) implies (1). Similarly (6) implies (2).

We have shown that in a finite plane of *order* n (this is the description of a finite projective plane with $n+1$ points on a line), the following properties hold:

(1) *There are* n^2+n+1 *lines.*

(2) *There are* n^2+n+1 *points.*

(3) *Every line contains* $n+1$ *points.*

(4) *Every point is on* $n+1$ *lines.*

(5) *There is one and only one line through two distinct points.*

(6) *Two distinct lines intersect in one and only one point.*

The last two properties are, of course, Axioms I and II. We now show that

5. *A system of points and lines satisfying* (1), (3) *and* (5), *or dually* (2), (4) *and* (6), *is a finite plane of order* n, *and satisfies the remaining properties.*

We suppose that there is a system of points and lines satisfying (1), (3) and (5). Let a point P lie on m lines. There are no points in the plane which are not on one of these lines. By (3), each one of these lines contains n points besides P. The total number of points in the plane is therefore $1+nm$. Since this is fixed, and n is given, m is fixed, and is the same for every point in the plane.

We want to show that $m = n+1$. Suppose that we count the total number of *incidences* in the plane, between points and lines. There are n^2+n+1 lines, by (1), and each line contains $n+1$ points, by (3). Hence there are $(n+1)(n^2+n+1)$ incidences. On the other hand, we saw that the plane contains $1+nm$ points, and each point is on m lines. Hence

$$(n+1)(n^2+n+1) = m(1+nm),$$

or $$(n+1-m)[1+n(n+1+m)] = 0,$$

giving $m = n+1$, from which (2) and (4) follow.

We must now deduce (6). From (5), two distinct lines cannot intersect in more than one point. If we can show that there is one point in which two distinct lines intersect, we shall have deduced (6).

But if l is any line in the plane, l contains $n+1$ points. Each of these points is on n other lines, besides l. Hence l intersects $n(n+1) = n^2+n$ lines. But, with l, this gives all the lines in the plane. We have therefore deduced (6). This proves that (1), (3) and (5) imply (2), (4) and (6). Dually it follows that (2), (4) and (6) imply (1), (3) and (5).

Exercise

1. A tennis match is played between two teams, each player playing one or more members of the other team. We are told that:
   (i) any two members of the same team have exactly one opponent in common,
   (ii) no two members of the same team play all the members of the other team between them.

Prove that two players who do not play each other have the same number of opponents. Deduce that any two players, whether in the same or different teams, have the same number of opponents.

5. Incidence matrices

We now describe an *incidence matrix* which can be associated with any finite projective plane π of order n.

Let $N = n^2+n+1$, and call the points of π: $P_1, P_2, ..., P_N$. Let the lines be called $l_1, l_2, ..., l_N$. We define *incidence numbers* a_{ij}, where

$$a_{ij} = 1 \quad \text{if} \quad P_i \in l_j,$$
$$a_{ij} = 0 \quad \text{if} \quad P_i \notin l_j,$$

and $i, j = 1, 2, ..., N$.

Then the incidence matrix A of π is defined to be the matrix

$$A = (a_{ij}) \quad (i, j = 1, 2, ..., N).$$

Before proving any properties of this matrix, we take the projective plane of order 2, with 3 points on each of its $2^2+2+1 = 7$ lines. The seven points are indicated in Fig. 65. The lines are:

$$l_1: (P_1 P_2 P_3), \quad l_2: (P_1 P_6 P_4),$$
$$l_3: (P_2 P_6 P_5), \quad l_4: (P_3 P_4 P_5),$$
$$l_5: (P_3 P_6 P_7), \quad l_6: (P_2 P_4 P_7),$$
$$l_7: (P_1 P_7 P_5).$$

The incidence matrix of this finite projective geometry is:

$$A = \begin{bmatrix} 1 & 1 & 0 & 0 & 0 & 0 & 1 \\ 1 & 0 & 1 & 0 & 0 & 1 & 0 \\ 1 & 0 & 0 & 1 & 1 & 0 & 0 \\ 0 & 1 & 0 & 1 & 0 & 1 & 0 \\ 0 & 0 & 1 & 1 & 0 & 0 & 1 \\ 0 & 1 & 1 & 0 & 1 & 0 & 0 \\ 0 & 0 & 0 & 0 & 1 & 1 & 1 \end{bmatrix}.$$

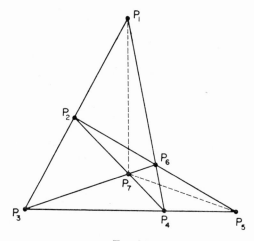

FIG. 65

The transpose is:

$$A' = \begin{bmatrix} 1 & 1 & 1 & 0 & 0 & 0 & 0 \\ 1 & 0 & 0 & 1 & 0 & 1 & 0 \\ 0 & 1 & 0 & 0 & 1 & 1 & 0 \\ 0 & 0 & 1 & 1 & 1 & 0 & 0 \\ 0 & 0 & 1 & 0 & 0 & 1 & 1 \\ 0 & 1 & 0 & 1 & 0 & 0 & 1 \\ 1 & 0 & 0 & 0 & 1 & 0 & 1 \end{bmatrix}.$$

A simple verification shows that

$$AA' = A'A = \begin{bmatrix} 3 & 1 & 1 & 1 & 1 & 1 & 1 \\ 1 & 3 & 1 & 1 & 1 & 1 & 1 \\ 1 & 1 & 3 & 1 & 1 & 1 & 1 \\ 1 & 1 & 1 & 3 & 1 & 1 & 1 \\ 1 & 1 & 1 & 1 & 3 & 1 & 1 \\ 1 & 1 & 1 & 1 & 1 & 3 & 1 \\ 1 & 1 & 1 & 1 & 1 & 1 & 3 \end{bmatrix}.$$

We prove in the general case for a projective plane of order n that

6. $$AA' = A'A = nI + S,$$

where I is the unit matrix, and S is the matrix with every entry $= 1$. Let $AA' = C$, where $C = (c_{rs})$, and

$$c_{rs} = \sum_{j=1}^{N} a_{rj} a_{sj},$$

by the definition of matrix multiplication and the transpose of a matrix. The rth row of A gives the incidences of the point P_r. This point is on $n+1$ lines, so that the rth row of A contains $n+1$ entries equal to 1, the remainder being zero. Since c_{rr} arises from the multiplication of corresponding elements, $c_{rr} = n+1$. If $r \neq s$, we see that $c_{rs} = 1$, since $a_{rj} a_{sj} = 0$ unless both $a_{rj} = 1$ and $a_{sj} = 1$. But $a_{rj} = a_{sj} = 1$ indicates that the line l_j contains both P_r and P_s. Given P_r and P_s there is exactly one line l_j containing both points. Hence $c_{rs} = 1$ for $r \neq s$, and since $c_{rr} = n+1$, we have proved that

$$AA' = nI + S.$$

A dual argument shows that

$$A'A = nI + S.$$

6. Subplanes of a finite plane

Let $\{P_i\}$ be a set of points in a projective plane π, amongst which there is a subset $\{l_j\}$ of lines. We assume that the three axioms are satisfied by these points and lines. If we consider the possible joins and intersections of these points and lines, we obtain further lines and points which also lie in π. These can be thought of as being *generated* by $\{P_i\}$ and $\{l_j\}$. Continuing thus, we have a projective plane π^* which is contained in (and may coincide with) π. We call π^* a *subplane* of π. If π is a finite projective plane, we can make deductions about the possible order of a subplane, which is naturally also finite.

7. *If a plane π of order n has a subplane π^* of order m, then $n = m^2$, or $n \geqslant m^2 + m$.*

We naturally exclude the case when $\pi^* = \pi$. Let l be a line of subplane π^*, and P a point of l not belonging to π^*. There are $m + 1$ points of π^* on l, and m^2 points of π^* not on l. We join P to each of these m^2 points of π^* not on l. Each of the m^2 lines we obtain must be different, since if two were the same, such a line would contain at least two points of π^*, and would therefore be a line of π^*. The point P, being the intersection of two lines of π^*, would lie in π^*, contrary to hypothesis. Hence through P there are at least $m^2 + 1$ distinct lines, namely l and the joins of P to the m^2 points of π^* not on l. Since there are $n + 1$ lines of π through P, we must have $n \geqslant m^2$.

If $n > m^2$, there will be at least one further line through P not containing any point of π^*. Call this line l'. Consider the intersections of l' with the $m^2 + m + 1$ lines of π^*. These $m^2 + m + 1$ intersections are all distinct, for if two were coincident, the intersection of two lines of π^* would be on l'. But two lines of π^* intersect in a point of π^*, and by hypothesis l' contains no point of π^*. It follows that l' contains at least $m^2 + m + 1$ points, and therefore $n \geqslant m^2 + m$.

Exercise

1. A finite geometry consisting of points and lines is subject to the following four axioms:
    (1) there is at least one point,
    (2) every line is a set of exactly two points,
    (3) every point lies on exactly two lines,
    (4) to a given line there are exactly three lines which do not intersect it (parallel lines).

Prove: (a) if two lines intersect they do so in just one point; (b) there is at least one line; (c) to a given line there are exactly two non-parallel lines; (d) there are exactly six lines; (e) there are exactly six points.

Show that there are two distinct models of the system, one consisting of two triangles and the other of a hexagon.

7. Affine planes

If one line and the points on it be removed from a projective plane, we obtain an *affine* plane. If the line is called ω, we call distinct lines which intersected on ω in the projective plane *parallel* lines in the affine plane. The projective plane being denoted by π, we call the affine plane obtained from it by the removal of ω the plane π_ω.

8. *If P is any point not on a line l, there is exactly one line through P which does not intersect l in* π_ω.

The line $l \neq \omega$, and therefore intersects ω in one point I in π. The line PI in π_ω, with the point I removed, is the line required.

This theorem can be restated in the form:

9. *Through P there passes exactly one line which is parallel to l.*

This line is called *the parallel to l through P*. It coincides with l when $P \in l$ if we frame our definition of *parallel* thus:

Two lines are parallel in an affine plane if they coincide, or, being distinct, if they have no point of intersection.

If l is parallel to m we write $l \| m$. We see that this relation is *reflexive*, since $l \| l$, and *symmetric*, since from $l \| m$ it follows that $m \| l$. It is also *transitive*, that is, if $l \| m$ and $m \| n$, we may deduce that $l \| n$. For if l and n are not parallel, the intersection $l \cap n$ exists, and $l \neq n$. Through the point $l \cap n$ there are consequently two distinct lines parallel to m, the lines l and n. This contradicts Theorem 9. Hence $\|$ is an equivalence relation, and we can divide the lines of the affine plane, by means of this relation, into mutually exclusive sets. In each set the lines are parallel to each other, but any two lines from two distinct sets have a point of intersection.

We can replace Axiom III, §1, for a projective plane by the axiom for an affine plane:

III*. *There are three non-collinear points.*

In fact, we saw in §2, Theorem 2, that a projective plane contains at least four lines, no three of which are concurrent. If ω is either one of l_1, l_2, l_5, l_6, in the notation of the proof of Theorem 2, the other three lines give, by their intersections, three non-collinear points.

8. Finite affine planes

A projective plane of order n has $n+1$ points on every one of its n^2+n+1 lines. If one of these lines is removed, we have a finite affine plane which contains n^2+n lines, but only n^2 points, since of the original n^2+n+1 points, $n+1$ have been removed.

Corresponding to each of the $n+1$ points on the deleted "line at infinity" there is a pencil of parallel lines. We therefore have $n+1$ pencils of parallel lines, and since $n+1$ lines pass through every point in the projective plane, each of these pencils contains n lines.

We pick out two of these pencils, and call them Π and Π'. We number the lines in Π: $0, 1, ..., n-1$, and we number the lines in Π' in a similar way. Through any point in the affine plane there passes one line of each of the $n+1$ pencils of parallel lines we have just described, and in particular just one line, say number i, of Π, and one line, say number j, of Π'. This point can be described therefore as the point (i,j), and all points in the affine plane have coordinates

$$(i,j) \quad (i,j = 0,1,...,n-1).$$

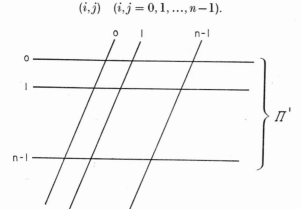

Fig. 66

We shall now define $n-1$ matrices associated with our finite plane. Let a point in the affine plane have coordinates (i,j). Through this point there passes one line of each of the remaining $n-1$ pencils of parallel lines. We assign the numbers $1,2,...,n-1$ to these pencils, and in each one of these pencils we number the lines $0,1,2,...,n-1$. We concentrate for the moment on the pencil with number λ $(1 \leqslant \lambda \leqslant n-1)$.

Through the point (i,j) there passes just one line of the pencil numbered λ. Let $l_{ij}^{(\lambda)}$ be the number assigned to this line in the pencil numbered λ. Then

$$0 \leqslant l_{ij}^{(\lambda)} \leqslant n-1.$$

We now consider the matrix

$$L^{(\lambda)} = (l_{ij}^{(\lambda)}) \quad (i,j = 0,...,n-1).$$

This is a square matrix of n rows and columns, and its entries consist of the integers $0,1,...,n-1$, the entry in row i and column j being $l_{ij}^{(\lambda)}$.

We consider row i of $L^{(\lambda)}$. We move along the line numbered i in the pencil Π, and consider the points of intersection with the lines numbered $0, 1, ..., n-1$ of Π'. Each of the points (i,j) produces an entry in row i of $L^{(\lambda)}$, and these entries are the numbers $0, 1, ..., n-1$ in some order. Similarly, column j of $L^{(\lambda)}$ is a permutation of the numbers $0, 1, ..., n-1$, since through every point of the line numbered i in Π (or the line numbered j in Π') there passes exactly one of the n lines of the parallel pencil numbered λ.

A matrix with this property ($n \geqslant 2$) is called an *n-rowed Latin square*.

Our finite affine plane produces $n-1$ Latin squares, and we consider their mutual relationship.

9. Orthogonal Latin squares

We consider two of these Latin squares, $L^{(\lambda)}$ and $L^{(\lambda')}$. Their entries arise from definite parallel pencils of lines, numbered λ and λ' respectively. Take the line numbered c in the λ pencil, and the line numbered c' in the λ' pencil. These lines intersect in just one point, and therefore determine a unique pair (i,j) of the plane. This means that, given λ, λ', c, c', the equations

$$l_{ij}^{(\lambda)} = c, \quad l_{ij}^{(\lambda')} = c'$$

are satisfied for exactly one pair (i,j).

To interpret this relationship, we imagine the matrix $L^{(\lambda')}$ superimposed on the matrix $L^{(\lambda)}$. Every entry in row i and column j of the matrices now has two numbers, instead of one, namely $l_{ij}^{(\lambda)}$ and $l_{ij}^{(\lambda')}$, and each of these numbers can be one of the set $0, 1, ..., n-1$. There are $n \times n = n^2$ possibilities which can arise in writing down a pair of integers (i,j) where $i, j = 0, 1, ..., n-1$, and the relationship above says that these n^2 possibilities are fulfilled when $L^{(\lambda)}$ and $L^{(\lambda')}$ are superimposed.

Two such Latin squares are said to be *orthogonal to each other*, and we have proved

10. *An affine plane of order n gives rise to $n-1$ mutually orthogonal n-rowed Latin squares.*

Exercise

1. Show that there is no pair of mutually orthogonal Latin squares of order 2, but there is a pair of mutually orthogonal Latin squares when $n = 3$.

Euler's problem of the 36 officers is very relevant at this point. Assuming that officers can have one of six distinct ranks, the problem is to choose 36 officers from 6 regiments, no two officers from the same regiment having the same rank, in such a way that when they are on parade in a 6×6 square, no column or row shall contain two officers of the same regiment or of the same rank.

If this problem were soluble, it would mean that we could write down two 6×6 Latin squares, one with entries denoting the 6 regiments, and the other with entries denoting the 6 ranks, and *these two Latin squares would be orthogonal.*

The existence of a finite plane of order 6 would give a solution of the Euler problem. It was proved by Tarry [14] in 1901, by the method of trial and error, that no such plane exists.

10. Construction of a finite affine plane

Let us see how, conversely, the existence of mutually orthogonal Latin squares of order n enables us to construct a finite affine plane of order n.

We suppose that we have $m-1$ Latin squares of order n,

$$L^{(\lambda)} = (l_{ij}^{(\lambda)}) \quad (\lambda = 1, ..., m-1),$$

where $i, j = 0, 1, ..., n-1$.

We call the n^2 entries (i, j) *Points*, and designate the following subsets as *Lines*:

I. *The sets where i has a fixed value:*
There are n of these.

II. *The sets where j has a fixed value:*
There are n of these.

III. *The sets (i, j) such that for a fixed λ, the entries in $L^{(\lambda)}$ have a fixed value.*

Every matrix $L^{(\lambda)}$ gives n Lines of this kind, each containing n Points.

Two distinct Lines of I have no Point of intersection, since if $i \neq i'$ we cannot have $(i, j) = (i', j')$. Similarly, two distinct Lines of II have no Point of intersection.

For a fixed λ, the point (i, j) gives only one value for $l_{ij}^{(\lambda)}$. Two distinct Lines of III, arising from the same value of λ, therefore have no Point of intersection.

We may therefore regard the Lines of I and II as forming two parallel pencils, and the Lines of III as forming $m-1$ parallel pencils. Each pencil contains n lines.

We show that any two Lines, from two distinct pencils of the $m+1$ considered, have a Point of intersection.

Keeping i' fixed, the set of points (i',j) of I gives a Line which meets the set of points (i,j'), where j' is fixed, in the Point (i',j'). Hence a Line of I intersects a Line of II.

If c is any one of the numbers $0, 1, ..., n-1$, and we move along row i' of $L^{(\lambda)}$, there is a unique j' such that $l_{i'j'}^{(\lambda)} = c$. Hence a Line of I intersects any Line of III. Similarly any Line of II intersects any Line of III.

Finally we show that any Line of III derived from $L^{(\lambda)}$ intersects any Line of III derived from $L^{(\lambda')}$. Let the first Line correspond to the entry $= c$, and the second Line to the entry (in $L^{(\lambda')}$) $= c'$. Since $L^{(\lambda)}$ and $L^{(\lambda')}$ are mutually orthogonal, there is a *unique* (i,j) such that $l_{ij}^{(\lambda)} = c$ and $l_{ij}^{(\lambda')} = c'$. The two Lines intersect at this Point (i,j).

Again, we must verify that through any given Point P there is a unique Line which is parallel to (does not intersect) a given Line. After the detailed explanations given above, we may safely leave this proof to the reader.

Exercise

1. With the definition of Point and Line given above, prove that through any given Point P there is a unique Line which does not intersect (is parallel to) a given Line.

Continuing our investigations, we see that the plane under consideration contains at least three non-collinear Points. In fact, the Points $(0,0)$, $(0,1)$ and $(1,0)$ do not lie on any of the Lines we have described.

We cannot complete our proof that all the axioms of a finite affine plane are satisfied until we have enough Lines. This depends on the number of mutually orthogonal Latin squares. Through a given Point (i',j') of the plane there pass, respectively, one Line of II and $m-1$ Lines of III which are distinct and intersect the Line (i'',j), where $i'' \neq i'$. The Line of II is given by the points (i,j'), and the $m-1$ Lines of III by $l_{ij}^{(\lambda)} = l_{i'j'}^{(\lambda)}$ $(\lambda = 1, 2, ..., m-1)$. These m Lines intersect the Line (i'',j) in distinct Points. But there are only n Points (i'',j). Hence $m \leqslant n$, and we deduce:

11. *There are at most $n-1$ mutually orthogonal Latin squares of order n.*

11. Complete orthogonal system of Latin squares

A system of $n-1$ mutually orthogonal n-rowed Latin squares is called a *complete orthogonal system* of Latin squares. With such a system, the affine plane we have set up contains $2n + n(n-1) = n^2 + n$ Lines, and we can invoke Theorem 5 (§4) to show that our final axiom: *through any two distinct Points there passes a unique Line*, is now satisfied. We therefore have a finite affine plane, and have proved:

12. *Every complete orthogonal system of n-rowed Latin squares represents an affine plane with n^2 points, and in this way we obtain all affine planes with n^2 points.*

Exercise

1. If $i_1 \neq i_2$, $j_1 \neq j_2$, deduce that in a complete orthogonal system of Latin squares there is one square for which the entries at (i_1, j_1) and (i_2, j_2) are the same.

The existence of finite projective (or affine) planes is therefore linked to the existence of complete orthogonal systems of Latin squares. It was conjectured by Euler that there are no mutually orthogonal Latin squares of order n if $n \equiv 2 \pmod 4$. The problem of the 36 officers and Tarry's result indicate that there is no finite affine plane of order $n = 6$. Apart from this isolated result, no restrictions on the possible orders of a finite plane were known until 1949, when Bruck and Ryser proved:

13. *If $n \equiv 1, 2 \pmod 4$, there cannot be a plane of order n unless n can be expressed as a sum of two integral squares, $n = a^2 + b^2$.*

For the proof, see Hall [**9**], p. 394.

Euler's conjecture has recently been proved to be false, by R. C. Bose and S. S. Shrikhande, in a paper entitled "On the falsity of Euler's conjecture about the non-existence of two orthogonal Latin squares of order $4t + 2$" (*Proc. Nat. Acad. Sci. U.S.A.*, **45**, 734–737 (1959)). See also a paper by the same authors and E. T. Parker entitled: "Further results on the construction of mutually orthogonal Latin squares and the falsity of Euler's conjecture" in *Canad. J. Math.*, **12**, 189–203 (1960).

Exercise

1. From the Latin square of order $n = 2$ obtain the finite affine plane with 4 points A, B, C, D, where $AB \parallel CD$, $BC \parallel AD$ and $AC \parallel BD$.

12. The existence of finite planes

Once coordinates are introduced into a projective plane (Ch. VI) we are assured of the existence of finite planes of orders $n = p^r$, where p is any prime and r is an integer. Let $GF(p^r)$ be a Galois field (see Appendix) containing $n = p^r$ elements. Then we may use these elements as coordinates, and since the elements are in a field, the resulting geometry is Desarguesian (Ch. VII, § 16, Th. 13). The field being commutative, the Pappus theorem also holds (Ch. VI, § 17, Th. 15).

Using homogeneous coordinates (Ch. VII), the point (x, y, z) is regarded as the same point as (kx, ky, kz) $(k \neq 0)$. Let $\lambda \neq 0$ be any *fixed* element of the field. Then there are n^2 points of the form (λ, α, β), where α and β vary over the elements of the field; there are n points of the form $(0, \lambda, \beta)$, and there is one point $(0, 0, \lambda)$, giving $n^2 + n + 1$ points in the plane. The number of points on the line $x = 0$ is $n + 1$ since, besides the points $(0, \lambda, \beta)$, there is also the point $(0, 0, \lambda)$.

Similarly we can define and obtain $n^2 + n + 1$ lines in the plane. This can be done without making use of all the field properties, and if we use a Veblen–Wedderburn system (Ch. VI, § 5) to coordinatize the plane, we may obtain non-Desarguesian geometries in which the Pappus theorem will naturally also not be valid. For further details see Veblen and Wedderburn (references in Hall [**9**]).

13. Collineations

We now consider, in a more formal manner, the question of *collineations* in a projective plane π.

A one-to-one transformation of the points of π, which we denote by α, so that

$$P \to P' = P^\alpha,$$

is said to be a *collineation* if the property of points being collinear is preserved. That is, if the points P, Q, R are collinear, the points P^α, Q^α, R^α are collinear. We use the index symbolism, P^α, for the transform of a point P under a transformation α, rather than the $P\alpha$ notation, which is sometimes ambiguous.

As we have already said, collineations have appeared in our first chapter, and we shall see here how important the idea of *perspectivity*, which also came earlier on, is in the development of projective geometry.

A *fixed point* (sometimes called *united point*) of a collineation α in π is a point P such that

$$P = P^\alpha.$$

A *fixed line* l is a line such that

$$l = l^\alpha.$$

It must be pointed out that although a line of fixed points is necessarily a fixed line, a fixed line does not necessarily consist of nothing but fixed points. What we can say is this:

14. *The line determined by two fixed points is a fixed line.*

15. *The point (of intersection) determined by two fixed lines is a fixed point.*

These are evident deductions from the fact that *a collineation preserves incidence properties.* If a point P lies on a line l, $P \in l$, then $P^\alpha \in l^\alpha$.

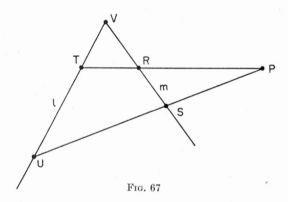

Fig. 67

16. *A collineation in a projective plane π which fixes every point on each of two distinct lines is the identical collineation.*

Let the collineation α fix every point on each of the two lines l and m, and let $l \cap m = V$. Let P be any point of π not on l or m. Take points R and S on m distinct from V, and let PR intersect l in T, and PS intersect l in U. (*It should be noted in this and all subsequent proofs that our axioms permit the suggested constructions.*)

The points R, S, T, U are fixed by α. Hence the lines TR and US are fixed by α. It follows that $TR \cap US = P$ is fixed by α. Since P is any point not already fixed by α, it follows that α is the identical collineation.

17. *A collineation in a projective plane π which fixes every point on one line, and two points not on the line, is the identical collineation.*

Let l be the line of fixed points, and U, V the two fixed points not on l. Let P be any point in π which is not on UV or l, and let

8

$PU \cap l = R$ and $PV \cap l = S$. Since P is not on UV, the lines UR and VS are distinct. For if $UR = VS$, the line UV meets $UR = VS$ in the distinct points U, V and therefore $UR = VS = UV$, so that P would lie on UV. Since U and R are distinct and fixed points,

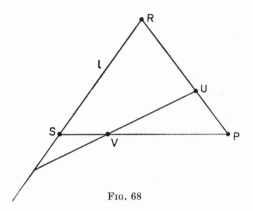

Fig. 68

the line UR is a fixed line. Similarly VS is a fixed line, and $P = RU \cap SV$ is a fixed point. Hence the collineation α fixes every point not on UV. The line UR therefore consists of fixed points, and this, together with l consisting of fixed points, brings us back to the conditions of the previous Theorem 16.

14. Main theorem on collineations

We have now reached the conclusion that a collineation fixing every point on a line can fix at most one point not on the line, if it is not the identical collineation. The main theorem clarifies this remark, and is now given:

18. *Let α be a collineation of the plane π which fixes every point on a line l. Then there is a point V such that α fixes V and every line through V.*

We suppose that α is not the identical collineation. By Theorem 17 there is at most one point not on l which is a fixed point. We suppose in the first place that α fixes a point V not on l. Then a line through V meets l in a point Q, and $Q \neq V$. Since V and Q are fixed points, the line VQ is fixed. Hence, every line through V is fixed by α. If there were a fixed line $m \neq l$, where m does not pass through V, then every point of m, being the intersection of fixed lines, would be fixed, and by Theorem 16, α would be the identity. By Theorem 17 there cannot be any point besides V, which is not on l, fixed by α.

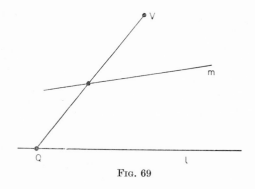

Fig. 69

If α fixes no point which is not on l, let P be a point not on l. Then P^α, the transform of P, is distinct from P, and P^α *does not lie on* l.

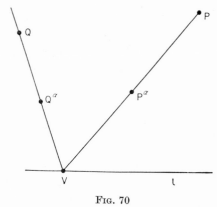

Fig. 70

We interrupt our proof to consider this statement. We know that if $P \in l$, then $P^\alpha \in l$, since $l^\alpha = l$. But to prove that if $P \notin l$, then $P^\alpha \notin l$ we must tighten up our definition of collineation. Since α is a one-to-one mapping of the points of π *onto* themselves, the *inverse* mapping α^{-1} exists (see Appendix), and if

$$P^\alpha = P'$$

then $$P = (P')^{\alpha^{-1}}.$$

Is this a collineation? It is if we say that the points P^α, Q^α, R^α are collinear *if and only if* P, Q, R are collinear. This is the definition of collineation we now adopt, and we see that with this new definition, if α is a collineation, so is α^{-1}.

If now we have a point fixed under α, say $Q^\alpha = Q$, then Q is fixed under α^{-1}. If l is a line fixed under α, it is fixed under α^{-1}. So that if we return to the proof above, and suppose that

$$P^\alpha \in l$$

this would imply that $\quad\quad P \in l^{\alpha^{-1}} = l,$

which is contrary to hypothesis.† Hence, to recapitulate, we suppose that α fixes no point not on l, and P is not on l. Then P^α is not on l. Hence the line $m = PP^\alpha$ cuts l in a point V distinct from P and P^α. The line $m = VP$, and

$$m^\alpha = V^\alpha P^\alpha = VP^\alpha = m.$$

We have therefore proved that every point P not on l lies on a fixed line.

Such a point cannot lie on two fixed lines, since it would be fixed. and P, by hypothesis, is not fixed. Now consider a point Q which is not on l or on m. Then Q also lies on a unique fixed line n. The intersection of m and n is a fixed point, and by hypothesis there are no fixed points not on l. Therefore n must intersect m in the point V lying on l.

The same argument shows that every fixed line passes through V.

Conversely, every line through V is a fixed line. For such a line, call it q, must contain a point, say R, not on l. Now R lies on a fixed line passing through V, and the only such line is VR.

Corollary: There are no other fixed elements besides l and the points on it, and V and the lines through it, unless α is the identity transformation.

Theorem 18 has a dual:

19. *If a collineation α of a projective plane π fixes a point V and all the lines through V, then there is a line l such that α fixes l and all the points on l.*

There are no further fixed points or lines if α is not the identity.

---

† Since α is one–one, $P^\alpha \in l$ leads to $P = P^\alpha$, the points of l being fixed. But the assumption that α^{-1} is a collineation is needed from § 15 onwards.

15. Central collineations

We now see the fundamental importance of the perspective transformations we introduced in Ch. I, § 10. These are sometimes

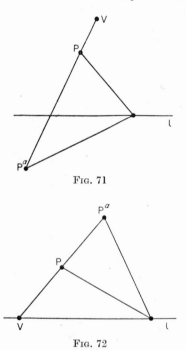

Fig. 71

Fig. 72

called *central collineations*, with *centre V* and *axis l*. If *V* does not lie on *l*, the collineation is called an *homology*, and if *V* lies on *l*, it is called an *elation*.

The collineations of a plane π onto itself form a group. If α, β are two collineations,

$$(P^\alpha)^\beta = P^{\alpha\beta}$$

defines the product $\alpha\beta$ of two collineations. The associative law holds for transformations, α has an inverse, and the identity 1 is the transformation in which every point of π is mapped onto itself.

We shall soon see that the collineations with centre V and axis l are not unique. We call such collineations (V, l)-*collineations*. Since a (V, l)-collineation fixes V, all lines through V, and all points on l, it is clear that:

(V, l)-*collineations form a group.*

We now see how a central collineation is determined.

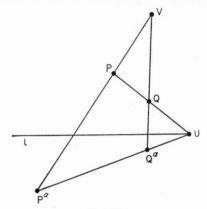

FIG. 73

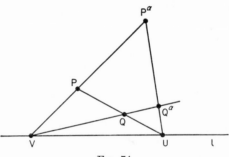

FIG. 74

20. *A central (V, l)-collineation is completely determined by the assignment of the map P^α of any point P not on l, where $P \neq V$, the points V, P, P^α being collinear.*

If there were two (V, l)-collineations, α and β, which mapped P on P^α, then the collineation $\alpha\beta^{-1}$ would have P as a fixed point, and continue to be a (V, l)-collineation. By Corollary, Theorem 18, $\alpha\beta^{-1} = 1$, or $\alpha = \beta$, which is what we wished to prove.

Figures 73 and 74 show how, given P and P^α, the transform Q^α of any given point Q is determined. The line PQ meets l at a fixed point U, and $(PQ)^\alpha = P^\alpha Q^\alpha$ passes through U and P^α. We also know that QQ^α passes through V. Hence $Q^\alpha = VQ \cap P^\alpha U$.†

† If a given collineation is *not* a central collineation, and therefore does not possess a line of fixed points, we cannot assume that l intersects l^α at a fixed point (see Ch. VIII, § 10).

The product of two (V, l)-elations is a (V, l)-elation. We now prove rather more:

21. *The product of two elations with the same axis l but distinct centres V and V' is an elation with axis l and centre $V'' \neq V, V'$.*

Let α be the (V, l)-elation and β the (V', l)-elation. Then $\alpha\beta$ is a central collineation, by Theorem 18, since it fixes all points on l. To show that $\gamma = \alpha\beta$ is an elation, with axis l, we must show that γ does not fix any point P not on l.

Suppose that $P\gamma = P$. Then

$$P^{\alpha\beta} = P, \quad P^{\alpha} = P^{\beta^{-1}}.$$

We know that V, P, P^{α} are collinear, and V', P, $P^{\beta^{-1}}$ are also collinear. The result just proved shows that

$$PP^{\alpha} = PP^{\beta^{-1}},$$

from which it follows, always supposing that $P \notin l$, that the intersections of these lines with l are the same. But $V \neq V'$. Hence $\gamma = \alpha\beta$ does not fix any point not on l, and is therefore an elation, with centre $V'' \in l$.

If $V'' = V$, then $\beta = \alpha^{-1}\gamma$ would be an elation with centre V. Hence $V'' \neq V$, and similarly $V'' \neq V'$.

16. Groups of collineations

Theorem 21 shows that all elations with axis l form a group. Because of the connection between elations and *translations* (see Ch. I, § 15), this group is called the *translation group with axis l*, and can be denoted by $G(l)$. If we are concentrating on a given elation-group with a fixed centre V and axis l, we use the notation $G(V, l)$.

We remark that since V, P, P^{α} are collinear, where P^{α} is the transform of a point P, the groups $G(V, l)$ and $G(V', l)$, where $V \neq V'$, can have no elation in common, except the identity.

In ordinary Cartesian geometry we assume the existence of translations parallel to the coordinate axes, and then also assume that the group of translations in the plane is commutative. The first assumption is that there are *two* centres on the line at infinity for which the elation groups $G(V, l)$, where l is the line at infinity, are not the identity. We *prove* that the commutativity of the translation group with axis l follows from this assumption.

22. *If for two distinct centres V and V' on an axis l the elation groups $G(V, l)$ and $G(V', l)$ are not the identity, then the entire translation group $G(l)$ is Abelian.*

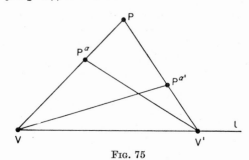

Fig. 75

Let α, α' be non-identical elations in the respective groups $G(V, l)$ and $G(V', l)$. Let P be any point of π not on l, and let m denote the line (VPP^{α}) and m' the line $(V'PP^{\alpha'})$,

$$m = (VPP^{\alpha}), \quad m' = (V'PP^{\alpha'}).$$

We consider the lines $m^{\alpha'}$ and m'^{α}. We have

$$m^{\alpha'} = (VP^{\alpha'}P^{\alpha\alpha'}), \quad m'^{\alpha} = (V'P^{\alpha}P^{\alpha'\alpha}).$$

Now the lines $VP^{\alpha'}$ and $V'P^{\alpha}$ are distinct, and therefore intersect in a point. We also know that the points

$$V, \quad P^{\alpha'}, \quad P^{\alpha'\alpha}$$

are collinear, and also the points

$$V', \quad P^{\alpha}, \quad P^{\alpha\alpha'}.$$

Hence $V'P^{\alpha}$ intersects $VP^{\alpha'}$ in $P^{\alpha\alpha'}$, and $VP^{\alpha'}$ intersects $V'P^{\alpha}$ in $P^{\alpha'\alpha}$. Therefore

$$P^{\alpha\alpha'} = P^{\alpha'\alpha},$$

and so $\alpha\alpha' = \alpha'\alpha$, and any element $\alpha \in G(V, l)$ permutes with any element $\alpha' \in G(V', l)$, if $V \neq V'$.

We now show that if $\beta \neq 1$ is another element of $G(V, l)$, then also $\alpha\beta = \beta\alpha$. We know by Theorem 21 that $\beta\alpha'$ is an elation with centre $V'' \neq V, V'$, so that we can apply the above argument to $\beta\alpha'$ and α, and show that they permute. From

$$\alpha(\beta\alpha') = (\beta\alpha')\,\alpha,$$

and
$$(\alpha\alpha') = (\alpha'\alpha),$$

we deduce that
$$\alpha\beta\alpha' = \beta\alpha\alpha',$$
whence
$$\alpha\beta = \beta\alpha.$$

Having proved that any two elements of distinct or identical elation groups with axis l permute, we can say that the translation group $G(l)$ is Abelian.

We can add to this theorem one on the orders of the elements of $G(l)$.

23. *With the conditions of the above theorem, every element $\neq 1$ of $G(l)$ is either of infinite order or of the same prime order p.*

If every element is of infinite order, there is no need to say more. But if $G(l)$ does contain elements of finite order, then there is an element α of prime order, p, say, where $\alpha \in G(V, l)$, and $\alpha^p = 1$. Let $\beta \neq 1$ be any element of $G(V', l)$, where $V \neq V'$. Then

$$\alpha\beta = \gamma \in G(V'', l), \quad \text{where} \quad V'' \neq V, V'.$$

Now, $(\alpha\beta)^p = \alpha^p\beta^p = \beta^p = \gamma^p$, since $G(l)$ is Abelian, and β^p is in $G(V', l)$, whereas γ^p is in $G(V'', l)$, where $V'' \neq V'$. We remarked above that the only element common to two elation groups with the same axis and distinct vertices is the identity. Hence $\beta^p = 1$. In the same way, from $\beta^p = 1$ we can deduce that $\alpha'^p = 1$, where α' is any element of $G(V, l)$. Hence, every element of $G(l)$ not the identity is of order p.

17. Central collineations and Desargues' theorem

There is an intimate connection between the existence of central collineations in a projective plane π and the validity of the Desargues theorem on perspective triangles, which we discussed in Ch. II, §3 onwards (see Fig. 76).

We suppose that we have two triangles, ABC, $A'B'C'$, and the lines AA', BB', CC' all pass through a point V. Two such triangles are said to be in perspective. Let the corresponding sides BC, $B'C'$ meet in L, let CA and $C'A'$ meet in M, and AB, $A'B'$ meet in N. The Desargues theorem states that L, M, N are collinear.

Without assuming this, suppose there is a central collineation, centre V and axis MN, which maps A on A'. By Theorem 20 the collineation is uniquely determined. Then since M is a fixed point, the line MA is mapped on MA'. Since V, C, C' are collinear, and $C \in MA$, $C' \in MA'$, the point C is mapped on C'. Similarly N is a fixed point, and NA is mapped on NA', so that B is mapped on B'.

In this collineation, therefore, A, B, C are mapped, respectively, on A', B', C'. The line BC is mapped on the line $B'C'$, and the intersection

$$L = BC \cap B'C'$$

is therefore a fixed point. Hence L either lies on MN, so that

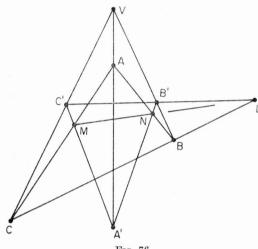

Fig. 76

L, M, N are collinear, giving the Desargues theorem, or $L = V$, since there are no other fixed points if the collineation is not the identity. If $L = V$, then

$$VBB' = LBB' = LC'B' = VC'B',$$

which would make $VB' = VC'$, which is contrary to hypothesis, since we assume that VAA', VBB' and VCC' are distinct.

Hence the existence of a central collineation with a given centre and axis involves the validity of the Desargues theorem, the two triangles involved having as centre and axis of perspective respectively the centre and axis of the collineation.

Conversely, suppose that the Desargues theorem is true for all pairs of triangles ABC, $A'B'C'$, where AA', BB' and CC' pass through a given point V, and $L = BC \cap B'C'$, $M = CA \cap C'A'$ (and therefore $N = AB \cap A'B'$) lie on a given line l. We prove that all possible (V, l) central collineations exist.

Let A, A' be any two distinct points collinear with V. We want to find the collineation, centre V and axis l, which maps A on A'.

If we can find such a collineation, we know that it is unique. We must define a mapping for every point of π, and show that this mapping is a collineation. We call the mapping α, so that $A^\alpha = A'$

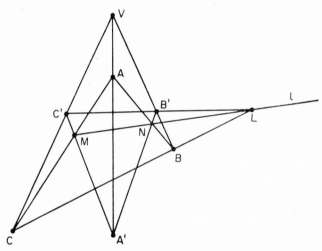

Fig. 77

For any point P on l we put $P^\alpha = P$. We also put $V^\alpha = V$.

If B is not on l, nor on VAA', we suppose that AB meets l in N, and that $A'N$ meets VB in B'. Then we put $B^\alpha = B'$.

This defines the mapping α for all points of π except those of VAA'. If C is not on l, and VC is distinct from VA and VB, we suppose that AC meets l in M, and that MA' meets VC in C', and we put $C^\alpha = C'$.

Now suppose that we begin to set up a collineation by mapping B on B'. Call this mapping β, so that $B^\beta = B'$. By Desargues' theorem applied to ABC and $A'B'C'$, since $N = AB \cap A'B'$ and $M = AC \cap A'C'$ are on l, we know that $L = BC \cap B'C'$ is on l. Hence $B'L$ meets VC in C', which implies that $C^\beta = C'$, so that

$$C^\alpha = C^\beta = C'.$$

Thus the mappings α and β agree on all lines such as VCC' for which they are both defined. Using β, we can define the map of all points on VAA', and so we have a mapping defined for all points of π.

We must now show that this mapping, which we still call α, is indeed a collineation, mapping collinear points into collinear points.

Using the same Fig. 77, with $A^\alpha = A'$, let m be an arbitrary line which does not pass through V or A, intersects l in L, and let B and C be two further points on m. By our definition, $B^\alpha = B'$, $C^\alpha = C'$ and $L^\alpha = L$, where $N = AB \cap A'B'$, and $M = AC \cap A'C'$ are on l. If we apply Desargues' theorem to ABC and $A'B'C'$, it follows that B', L, C' are collinear.

This tells us that the mapping α takes points C of $m = LB$ into points of LB'. Since α is not defined for points on VAA', we must apply the mapping β to the point of intersection of LB and VAA', and β maps this point on the point of intersection of LB' and VAA', so all is well.

The definition of α involves l being mapped on itself, since all points on l are defined as fixed points, and, by definition also, V is mapped on itself, and any point P on a line through V is mapped onto a point on the same line through V. Hence lines through V are mapped on themselves, and all lines in π have been accounted for. We have therefore proved

24. *In a projective plane π there are all possible collineations with a given centre V and a given axis l if, and only if, the Desargues theorem holds for all pairs of triangles with centre of perspective V and two pairs of corresponding sides (and therefore also the third pair) intersecting on l.*

We saw in Ch. II, §4 that Desargues' theorem is universally valid in a projective plane π if π can be embedded in a projective space of three dimensions. But we also saw, Ch. II, §5, that there are non-Desarguesian projective planes.

18. (V, l)-transitivity

If, for a given centre V and axis l in a projective plane π, all possible central collineations with centre V and axis l exist, we say that π is (V, l)-*transitive*.

This implies that, given any two distinct points P, P', neither of which coincides with V or lies on l, such that V, P, P' are collinear, there is an element α in the group $G(V, l)$ of collineations with centre V and axis l such that $P^\alpha = P'$.

Alternatively, the statement that π is (V, l)-transitive means that on any line $m \neq l$ passing through V, the (V, l)-collineations permute transitively all the points of m except for the points V and $l \cap m$, which are necessarily fixed points.

19. The minor Desargues theorem

In the discussions above about the connection between the theorem of Desargues and central collineations, it must be understood that the possibility $V \in l$, in which case the collineation is called an *elation* (§ 15), is always present. If we consider elations, the theorem of Desargues deals with two triangles ABC, $A'B'C'$, where AA', BB', CC' all pass through a point V, the three points $L = BC \cap B'C'$, $M = CA \cap C'A'$ and $N = AB \cap A'B'$ lie on a line l, *and V also lies on l*. The theorem in this case is called *the minor Desargues theorem*. A reference to Ch. II, § 4, Exercise 1, shows that there are a number of equivalent specializations of the general Desargues configuration.

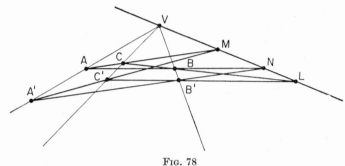

Fig. 78

Elations and the minor Desargues theorem will play an important part in the subsequent chapter. We add a final theorem on elations with a common axis (see Fig. 79).

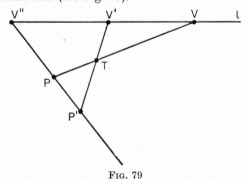

Fig. 79

25. *If a plane π is (V, l)-transitive and (V', l)-transitive for two centres $V \neq V'$ on l, then π is (V'', l)-transitive for every V'' on l.*

Let P, P' be any two distinct points collinear with V''. Let $PV \cap P'V' = T$. By hypothesis $\alpha \in G(V, l)$ such that $P^\alpha = T$, and $\alpha' \in G(V', l)$ such that $T^{\alpha'} = P'$. By Theorem 21 the product $\alpha\alpha' = \alpha''$ is an elation and

$$P^{\alpha''} = P^{\alpha\alpha'} = T^{\alpha'} = P'.$$

Since $PP' \cap l = V''$, the centre of α'' is V''. Hence π is (V'', l)-transitive.

If π is (V, l)-transitive for every point V on a fixed line l, we say that π is *a translation plane with respect to* l.

26. *If π is a translation plane with respect to two lines intersecting in a point U, then it is a translation plane with respect to every line of π passing through U.*

To prove this theorem, we need to make use of a notion we have not needed so far, the effect of a collineation ρ of the plane π on a given central collineation α, and we first prove:

27. *If α is a central collineation with axis l and centre V, the collineation ρ applied to the points of π transforms α into the central collineation $\rho^{-1}\alpha\rho$ with axis l^ρ and centre V^ρ.*

Under the central collineation α, the point P is mapped on P^α. Applying the collineation ρ to the points of the plane,

$$P^\rho \to (P^\alpha)^\rho = P^{\alpha\rho}$$

and

$$(P^{\rho^{-1}})^\rho \to (P^{\rho^{-1}})^{\alpha\rho},$$

that is,

$$P \to P^{\rho^{-1}\alpha\rho}.$$

This gives the symbol $\rho^{-1}\alpha\rho$ for the effect of the transform, under ρ, of the central collineation α. The lines $P^{\rho^{-1}} P^{\rho^{-1}\alpha}$ which passed through V will pass through V^ρ after the collineation ρ has been applied, and the lines $m^{\rho^{-1}}$, $m^{\rho^{-1}\alpha}$ which met on l will meet on l^ρ. Hence $\rho^{-1}\alpha\rho$ is a central collineation with axis l^ρ and centre V^ρ.

Since a collineation preserves incidences, if $V \in l$, then $V^\rho \in l^\rho$, so that an elation remains an elation after the transformation.

We now return to Theorem 26. Let l, m be the two lines intersecting at U. The plane π is a translation plane with respect to both l and m. Let n be a third distinct line through U, and let V'' be any point on n, distinct from U. Let $VV''V'$ be any line through V'' which meets l in $V \neq U$ and meets m in $V' \neq U$. Since π is a translation plane with respect to l, there exists an elation centre V and axis l which maps V' on V'', and therefore maps m on n. Call this elation ρ. Then

$$(V')^\rho = V'', \quad m^\rho = n.$$

By the theorem proved above (Theorem 27), the transform under ρ of any elation centre V' and axis m is an elation centre V'' and axis n. We have to show that all possible (V'', n)-elations can be obtained in this way.

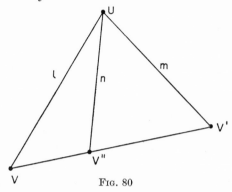

Fig. 80

If α is any element of $G(V', m)$, it transforms into the elation $\rho^{-1}\alpha\rho$ with centre V'' and axis n. We wish to show that α can be so determined that

$$P^{\rho^{-1}\alpha\rho} = P',$$

where P and P' are any two points distinct from V'' and collinear with V''. This condition can be written

$$(P^{\rho^{-1}})^\alpha = (P')^{\rho^{-1}},$$

or

$$Q^\alpha = Q',$$

where now $Q = P^{\rho^{-1}} \neq V'$ and $Q' = (P')^{\rho^{-1}} \neq V'$, and Q, Q' are collinear with V'. But since all possible elations with centre V' and axis m exist, α can be determined to satisfy this condition, and we have therefore proved that all possible (V'', n)-elations exist, where V'' is any point on n. Hence π is also a translation plane for n.

Corollary: If π is a translation plane with respect to three lines which are not concurrent, then it is a translation plane with respect to every line in the plane.

Let the three given lines form the triangle ABC, and let l be any other line in the plane. If l passes through A, B or C the corollary follows from the theorem just proved. Suppose therefore that $l \cap BC = U$, where $U \neq B$, $U \neq C$. The corollary holds for the line AU, and since it holds for the lines UA and UB, it holds for the line l also (see Fig. 81).

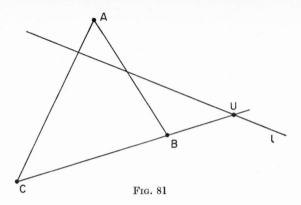

Fig. 81

20. Collineations in finite planes

If we assume nothing about a finite projective plane beyond the axioms of §1, and the consequent deductions, it might be thought that there is little that can be proved about the possible collineations of the plane. Of course, if we may assume coordinates, and take π to be a projective plane over some Galois field (see §12), the problem is simpler. But Reinhold Baer has shown that much may be discovered in the case where the minimum is assumed. In this section we give some results which do not involve any deep knowledge of the theory of groups.

The results of §13 on collineations were proved on the basis of the axioms for a projective plane, and did not assume at any stage that a line contains an infinite number of points. In particular the simple theorems, that the join of two fixed points is a fixed line, and the intersection of two fixed lines is a fixed point are true in a finite plane. But in a finite plane we know that if a line contains $n+1$ points, every line contains $n+1$ points, $n+1$ lines pass through every point, and the number of lines = number of points = n^2+n+1 (§4, Th. 4). The number of fixed points under a collineation α is therefore finite. Let it be $N(\alpha)$. We prove:

28. *The number of fixed lines under the collineation α is also $N(\alpha)$.*

The point P and the line l are said to form a *pair* with respect to α if P is on l and also on l^{α}. Denote by $M(\alpha)$ the number of distinct pairs with respect to α. Let $N'(\alpha)$ denote the number of fixed lines of α. If l is a fixed line of α, then (P,l) is a pair if, and only if, P is on l. Since every line of π contains $n+1$ points, the number of pairs (P,l), where l is a fixed line of α, is $(n+1)\,N'(\alpha)$. If l is not a fixed line of α, then l and l^α meet in a unique point $l \cap l^\alpha$, and $(l \cap l^\alpha, l)$ is the only pair containing l. Hence, since there are $1 + n + n^2$ lines in π,

$$1 + n + n^2 - N'(\alpha)$$

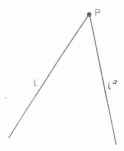

FIG. 82

is the number of pairs (P, l) where l is not a fixed line. Combining these results, the number of distinct pairs $M(\alpha)$ is given by:

$$M(\alpha) = (n+1) N'(\alpha) + 1 + n + n^2 - N'(\alpha)$$
$$= nN'(\alpha) + 1 + n + n^2.$$

The point P and the line l are said to form a *couple* with respect to α if l contains both P and P^α. We denote by $M'(\alpha)$ the number of

FIG. 83

distinct couples with respect to α. Since *couple* is the dual of *pair*, the dual of the proof above gives

$$M'(\alpha) = nN(\alpha) + 1 + n + n^2.$$

Now if we apply the transformation α^{-1} to a *pair* configuration we obtain Fig. 84 which shows that we have a (P, l) *couple* configuration with respect to α^{-1}, and if we apply the α transformation to a

9

couple under α^{-1}, also shown in Fig. 84, we obtain a *pair* under the α transformation. Hence the point P and the line l form a pair with respect to α if, and only if, they form a couple with respect to α^{-1}. Therefore

$$M(\alpha) = M'(\alpha^{-1}).$$

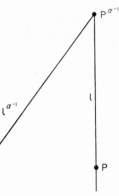

FIG. 84

By definition of α^{-1}, the collineations α and α^{-1} have the same fixed elements, so that

$$N(\alpha) = N(\alpha^{-1}).$$

Combining these results,

$$M(\alpha) = nN'(\alpha) + 1 + n + n^2 = M'(\alpha^{-1})$$
$$= nN(\alpha^{-1}) + 1 + n + n^2$$
$$= nN(\alpha) + 1 + n + n^2,$$

so that $$N(\alpha) = N'(\alpha),$$

the number of fixed points is equal to the number of fixed lines, which is what we wished to prove.

21. Involutions in finite projective planes

Our final theorem in this section involves collineations of order 2, which are called *involutions*. For such collineations α, we have $\alpha^2 = 1$, the identity transformation.

29. *Let α be an involution in a projective plane of order n. There are two possibilities:*

1. $n = m^2$, *and the fixed points and lines of α form a subplane of order m, or*

2. *α is a central collineation. In this case, if n is odd, α is an homology, and if n is even, α is an elation.*

We first prove that every point of π lies on a fixed line with respect to α, when α is an involution. If P is not a fixed point, $P^\alpha \neq P$, and since $P^{\alpha^2} = P$, α fixes the line PP^α, which is therefore a fixed line through P.

If P is a fixed point, join P to Q, another point. If the line PQ is fixed, we have finished. If not, $Q^\alpha \neq Q$, and Q^α does not lie on PQ.

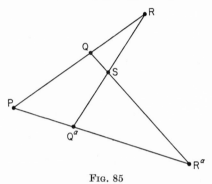

Fig. 85

If R is a third point on PQ, the point R^α lies on PQ^α. We have

$$(QR^\alpha)^\alpha = Q^\alpha R,$$

$$(Q^\alpha R)^\alpha = QR^\alpha,$$

so that α interchanges the lines QR^α and RQ^α. Hence $S = QR^\alpha \cap Q^\alpha R$ is a fixed point,† distinct from P, and PS is a fixed line through P.

By a dual argument, every line passes through a fixed point.

The line joining a pair of fixed points is a fixed line, and the intersection of two fixed lines is a fixed point. The fixed elements of a projective plane π form a closed subset under the operations of joining and intersecting. Hence if there exist four fixed points, no three on a line, the fixed elements of α form a proper subplane π^* of π (§ 6). We suppose that this is the case, and that π^* is of order m.

By § 6, Theorem 7, $n \geqslant m^2$, and if $n > m^2$ there is a line of π which does not pass through any point of π^*. But we saw above that all lines of π pass through a fixed point. This contradiction shows that $n = m^2$, and proves part (1) of the theorem.

† This argument is quite distinct from the fallacious one that under any collineation α, l and l^α intersect in a fixed point (see footnote to § 15, Th. 20).

We now consider the case where there are no four fixed points forming a quadrangle. We prove, first of all, that there is a line containing three fixed points. Any line l contains a fixed point P. Take a line m not through P. This contains a fixed point $Q \neq P$.

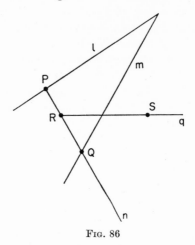

Fig. 86

The line n joining the fixed points P and Q is a fixed line. Choose a third point R on n. If R is fixed, n is the line we are seeking. If R is not fixed, a line q through R contains a fixed point S which is not on n. We therefore have a triangle PQS of fixed points. Consider any line u which does not pass through any one of P, Q or S. Then u contains a fixed point U. If U is not on one of the sides of the triangle PQS, then we have a quadrangle $PQSU$, and we are back in case (1). Hence U must lie on a side of the triangle PQS, and we have a line containing three fixed points.

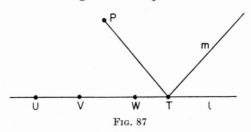

Fig. 87

Let l be a line containing three fixed points, U, V, W. If there were even two more fixed points not on l, we should be back in case (1), with a quadrangle of fixed points. Hence there is either one fixed point not on l or none. If there is a fixed point not on l, call it P.

If T is any point of l, there is a line m through T distinct from l, or from TP, if P exists. This line contains a fixed point. Since P is the only possible fixed point not on l, and $m \neq TP$, the fixed point must be T. Hence every point of l is fixed, and by §14, Theorem 18, the collineation α is a central collineation with axis l.

The plane π contains n^2 points which are not on l. If P is one of these points, and $P \neq P^\alpha$, then since $(P^\alpha)^\alpha = P$, we can divide all the points of π which do not lie on l into pairs. If n is odd, n^2 is odd, and one point will remain. This is a fixed point, and α is an homology.

If n is even, α fixes an even number of points not on l, and so fixes at least two or none. Since the first possibility is excluded, there are no points fixed which are not on l, and α is therefore an elation. This concludes the proof.

CHAPTER VI

THE INTRODUCTION OF COORDINATES INTO A PROJECTIVE PLANE

1. The method

There are various ways of introducing a coordinate system into a projective plane. Here we shall follow the method of Marshall Hall, which is the simplest, and leads to a searching investigation into the structure of projective planes.

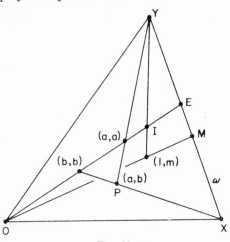

FIG. 88

Let π be any projective plane, and select four points X, Y, O, I, no three on a line. Call the line XY *the line at infinity* ω.

The line OI will be our unit line $y = x$. Assign coordinates $(0,0)$ to O, $(1,1)$ to I, the single coordinate (1) to the point E where OI meets ω. For other points of OI assign the coordinates (b,b), where we take different symbols b for different points. No other restriction is imposed at the moment.

For a point P not on ω, let XP meet OI in (b,b), and let YP intersect OI in (a,a). Then we assign the coordinates (a,b) to P. This rule assigns the coordinates (c,c) to any point of OI.

All points on YI have coordinates $(1, m)$. If the line joining $(0, 0)$ and $(1, m)$ meets ω in a point M, we assign the single coordinate (m) to M. We may think of (m) intuitively as a slope, as in elementary coordinate geometry.

We have now assigned coordinates to every point except Y, and we arbitrarily assign the single coordinate (∞) to this point.

The lines of the plane will be used to define algebraic operations on the system of coordinates. If (x, y) is a finite point of OI, we have $y = x$, and so we take $y = x$ as the equation of OI. A line through $Y \neq \omega$ will have the property that all its finite points (x, y) have the same x-coordinate, say $x = c$, and we take this as its equation. Similarly, a line through $X \neq \omega$ has the equation $y = d$. The lines OY, OX, in particular, are given by $x = 0$ and $y = 0$.

Consider the line joining $(0, b)$ and the point $E = (1)$. If (x, y) is any finite point on this line, we *define* a binary operation of addition by putting

$$y = x + b,$$

and taking this as the equation of the line.

It is clear that

$$0 + b = b.$$

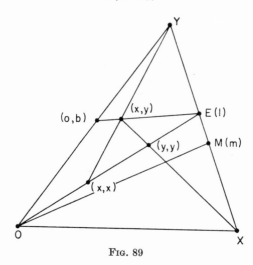

FIG. 89

To find $b + 0$, we join $(0, 0)$ to E. Then the y-coordinate when $x = b$ is $y = b$, so that

$$b + 0 = b.$$

If (x, y) is a finite point on the line joining $O = (0, 0)$ and (m), we *define* a binary operation of multiplication, putting

$$y = xm,†$$

and taking this as the equation of the line. Since the point (m) on ω was obtained by joining O to $(1, m)$,

$$1m = m.$$

To find $m1$, we consider the line joining O to E. For all points on this line, $y = x$, so that

$$m1 = m.$$

We have

$$0m = 0$$

since $(0, 0)$ is on $y = xm$, and the line joining O to X is $y = 0$ so that

$$m0 = 0.$$

Any line not through Y will intersect ω in some point (m), and OY in some point $(0, b)$. If (x, y) is any point on this line, we *define* a ternary operation

$$y = \mathbf{T}[x, m, b],$$

and take this as the equation of the line. Both addition and multiplication, as previously defined, are special cases of this ternary relation. In fact,

$$x + b = \mathbf{T}[x, 1, b],$$

and

$$xm = \mathbf{T}[x, m, 0].$$

We saw above that the elements 0 and 1 satisfy:

$$0 + a = a + 0 = a,$$

$$0m = m0 = 0,$$

$$1m = m1 = m.$$

2. Ternary rings

We have made little use of the properties of the plane π so far, and we show now that π can be represented by a ternary ring $\mathbf{T}$ whose ternary operation satisfies certain properties, and, conversely, that a ternary ring with these properties determines a plane uniquely.

† See § 18, where we remark that we could equally well take $y = mx$ for the equation of the line.

The main theorem is:

1. *For every choice of a quadrangle X, Y, O, I in a plane π, there is determined a ternary ring* **T**. *The elements of* **T** *include a zero, 0, and a unit $1 \neq 0$. The ternary operation* **T**$[x, m, b]$ *satisfies the following laws:*

1. $$\mathbf{T}[0, m, c] = \mathbf{T}[a, 0, c] = c.$$

2. $$\mathbf{T}[1, m, 0] = \mathbf{T}[m, 1, 0] = m.$$

3. *Given a, m, c, there exists exactly one z such that* $\mathbf{T}[a, m, z] = c$.

4. *If $m_1 \neq m_2$, b_1, b_2 are given, there exists a unique x such that*
$$\mathbf{T}[x, m_1, b_1] = \mathbf{T}[x, m_2, b_2].$$

5. *If $a_1 \neq a_2$, c_1, c_2 are given, then there exists a unique pair m, b such that*
$$\mathbf{T}[a_1, m, b] = c_1, \quad and \quad \mathbf{T}[a_2, m, b] = c_2.$$

The ternary ring is constructed as above, with an operation $\mathbf{T}[x, m, b]$. Properties 1 and 2 are immediate consequences of the definition. Property 3 says that the line joining (m) and (a, c) meets OY in a unique point $(0, z)$. Property 4 says that two lines $y = \mathbf{T}[x, m_1, b_1]$ and $y = \mathbf{T}[x, m_2, b_2]$, with different slopes m_1 and m_2, intersect in a unique finite point. Finally, property 5 says that if (a_1, c_1) and (a_2, c_2) are two finite points, with $a_1 \neq a_2$, then there is a unique line of the form $y = \mathbf{T}[x, m, b]$ passing through them.

Conversely, let us suppose that we are given a ternary ring **T**, satisfying the properties $1, \ldots, 5$. We construct finite points (a, b), and infinite points (m) and (∞), where a, b and m range over the elements of **T**. A line ω, the line at infinity, is to contain all the points (m) and (∞), and no other points.

All points (c, y) with c fixed, and also the point (∞), are to be the points of a line $x = c$.

The point (m) and the points (x, y) such that $y = \mathbf{T}[x, m, b]$ for fixed m and b are to be the points of the line $y = \mathbf{T}[x, m, b]$. We note that when $m = 0$ the lines $y = b$ are included amongst these lines, by property 1.

We have to show that the points and lines, defined as above, satisfy the axioms for a projective plane, that two distinct points define just one line, that two distinct lines intersect in only one point, and that the plane contains a quadrangle. We take the last requirement first.

The four points (∞), (0), $(0, 0)$ and $(1, 1)$ are distinct, and no three lie on any one of the lines described above. In fact, these points are on the line at infinity, the lines $y = 0$ and $x = 0$, the lines $y = 1$ and $x = 1$, and the line $y = x$, and none of these six lines, each of which contains two of the four points, contains a third.

For two infinite points, there is just one line joining them, the line at infinity. For the infinite point (m), and the finite point (a, c), there exists, by property 3, exactly one b such that $T[a, m, b] = c$. The line $y = T[x, m, b]$ therefore goes through (m) and the point (a, c). If there were two distinct lines $y = T[x, m, b]$ and $y = T[x, m, b']$ through the point (m) and the point (a, c), this would conflict with property 3.

Through two finite points (a_1, c_1) and (a_2, c_2), we have the line $x = a_1$, if $a_1 = a_2$. If $a_1 \neq a_2$, property 5 shows the existence of a unique line $y = T[x, m, b]$ containing both points.

The intersections of distinct lines are easily dealt with. Property 4 ensures that two lines with distinct slopes have a unique point of intersection. The only lines which do not enter into this category are the line at infinity and the lines $x = c$. All lines $x = c$ meet the line at infinity in the point (∞), and $x = c$ meets the line $y = T[x, m, b]$ in the unique point $(c, T[c, m, b])$.

We have shown, therefore, that a ternary ring with the given properties defines a projective plane.

3. Introduction of the minor Desargues theorem

If we introduce some structure into our projective plane, we shall obtain further properties of the ternary ring coordinatizing it. We naturally hope that our equations for lines will become linear, and this is what happens when we assume the minor Desargues theorem, with centre Y and axis ω (Ch. V, §19). In terms of elations, we assume that π is (Y, ω)-transitive, and then we see that for the corresponding coordinatizing ring T the following theorem holds:

2. *A plane is (Y, ω)-transitive only if, in the corresponding coordinatizing ternary ring T, we have*

1. $T[a, m, b] = am + b$, *and*

2. *Addition is a group.*

We suppose that π is (Y, ω)-transitive. In Fig. 90 we take YQV as $x = 0$, where V is $(0, 0)$, $Q = (0, b)$, $X = (0)$, $E = (1)$, $M = (m)$. Then MQ is $y = T[x, m, b]$.

Take P on MQ as $P = (a, T[a, m, b])$. The line VM is $y = xm$, and EQ is $y = x + b$ whilst YP is $x = a$. The point $U = VM \cap YP$ is $U = (a, am)$, and UX is $y = am$. The line UX intersects VE, which is

$y = x$, in $W = (am, am)$. The line YW, which is $x = am$, intersects QE, which is $y = x + b$, in $R = (am, am + b)$.

If P, R, X lie on a line, since RX is $y = am + b$, and

$$P = (a, \mathbf{T}[a, m, b]),$$

we shall have $$\mathbf{T}[a, m, b] = am + b.$$

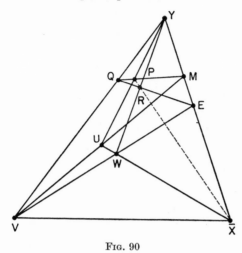

FIG. 90

Since the plane is (Y, ω)-transitive, the minor Desargues theorem holds for the vertex Y and the axis ω (Ch. V, §17, Th. 24). The triangles PQR and UVW are in perspective from the vertex Y, and $QP \cap VU = M$, $QR \cap VW = E$, and UW meets ω at X. Hence PR also passes through X.

What we have done is to set up an elation β, with centre Y and axis ω, which maps V on Q, so that $V^\beta = Q$. We determine the effect of this elation on a general point (a, c).

The line VE, $y = x$, becomes the line QE, $y = x + b$, so that

$$[y = x]^\beta = [y = x + b].$$

Lines through Y are unchanged, so that

$$[x = c]^\beta = [x = c].$$

Therefore,

$$[c, c]^\beta = [c, c + b].$$

Hence $$[y = c]^\beta = [y = c + b],$$

and since $$[x = a]^\beta = [x = a],$$

it follows that

$$(a, c)^\beta = (a, c+b).$$

Now let γ be the (Y, ω)-elation determined by the mapping

$$(0, 0)^\gamma = (0, d).$$

Then, as above,

$$(u, v)^\gamma = (u, v+d).$$

Hence, for the product elation, $\beta\gamma$, we find that

$$(0, 0)^{\beta\gamma} = [(0, 0)^\beta]^\gamma = (0, b)^\gamma = (0, b+d),$$

so that

$$(a, c)^{\beta\gamma} = [a, c+(b+d)].$$

But we also have

$$[(a, c)^\beta]^\gamma = (a, c+b)^\gamma$$

$$= [a, (c+b)+d].$$

Hence *addition satisfies the associative law*:

$$c+(b+d) = (c+b)+d.$$

Looking back at Fig. 89, the definition of addition with reference to points on the line joining $(0, b)$ to (1) shows that in

$$y = x+b$$

any two of the three quantities (x, y, b) uniquely determine the third. Addition is therefore a *quasi-group*.† There is a zero 0, such that

$$0+a = a+0.$$

Addition is therefore also a *loop*,† and the preceding remark ensures the existence of an inverse $-a$ for any element a. As we have just shown that addition is associative, this adds up to the theorem that *addition is a group*.

4. The converse theorem

The converse of the preceding theorem is true:

3. *If a ternary ring* **T**, *defined over* π, *satisfies the conditions*

  1. $\mathbf{T}[a, m, b] = am+b$,

  2. *Addition is a group,*

then π *is* (Y, ω)-*transitive.*

  † See Appendix for definition of these terms.

For any element b in **T**, define a mapping $\beta = \beta(b)$ as follows:

For points: $$(\infty)^\beta = (\infty),$$
$$(m)^\beta = (m),$$
$$(a, c)^\beta = (a, c+b).$$

For lines: $$(\omega)^\beta = (\omega),$$
$$[x = a]^\beta = [x = a],$$
$$[y = xm + t]^\beta = [y = xm + (t+b)].$$

This mapping is a collineation, since if (a, c) is on $y = xm + t$, then $c = am + t$, where

$$c + b = (am + t) + b = am + (t + b),$$

and so $(a, c + b)$ is on $y = xm + (t + b)$. This disposes of the lines other than the line at infinity and the lines $x = a$, and these are unchanged by the collineation.

Finally, this collineation is a (Y, ω)-elation, and it takes $(0, 0)$ into $(0, b)$. Since b is arbitrary, the plane π is (Y, ω)-transitive.

5. Veblen–Wedderburn systems

As we saw in Ch. V, §19 a *translation plane* with respect to the line ω is a plane π such that π is (Y, ω)-transitive for every point of ω. If we assume that π is a translation plane with respect to ω, we shall obtain further properties of our ternary ring **T**. In fact, we shall show that it is a *Veblen–Wedderburn* system. This means that:

1. Addition is an Abelian group.
2. Multiplication (excluding 0) is a loop.
3. $(a + b) m = am + bm$.
4. If $r \neq s$, $xr = xs + t$ has a unique solution x.
5. $\mathbf{T}[a, m, b] = am + b$.

Such a system was first described in a paper by O. Veblen and J. H. M. Wedderburn (see Hall [9] for references).

We now prove that

4. *A plane π is a translation plane with respect to the axis ω only if the corresponding ternary ring is a Veblen–Wedderburn system.*

By Ch. V, §19, Theorem 25, π will be a translation plane with axis ω if it is (Y, ω)-transitive and also (X, ω)-transitive. By §3, Theorem 2, we know that $\mathbf{T}[a, m, b] = am + b$.

In the proof of §4, Theorem 3, we showed the existence of an elation $\beta(b)$ for every b in $\mathbf{T}$ which maps any (a, c) into $(a, c+b)$. Again, by Ch. V, §16, Theorem 22, the entire translation group is Abelian, whence

$$\beta(b)\,\beta(d) = \beta(d)\,\beta(b),$$

and so

$$(a, c+b+d) = (a, c+d+b).$$

Hence $$b+d = d+b,$$

and thus addition in $\mathbf{T}$ is Abelian.

We saw that multiplication was defined with respect to the line joining $(0, 0)$ to (m) in §1, and in $y = xm$, if none of the three quantities is 0, any two of x, y, m determine the third uniquely. Since also there is a unit 1, such that $1m = m1 = m$, we see that multiplication, excluding 0, is a loop.

So far we have proved conditions (1), (2) and (5). All that (4) says is that if $r \neq s$, the lines $y = xr$ and $y = xs+t$ intersect in a unique finite point, which is the case. We have therefore only condition (3) left, and here we must use the fact that π is a translation plane for ω. So far we have only used the (Y, ω)-transitiveness.

Let b be an arbitrary element of $\mathbf{T}$, and consider the elation with centre X and axis ω taking $(0, 0)$ into $(b, 0)$. In this case all lines through X are unchanged, and if we denote the elation by α,

$$[y = a]^{\alpha} = [y = a].$$

The line $y = x$ through $(0, 0)$ and (1) becomes the line through $(b, 0)$ and (1). Its equation is $y = x - b$, since it has slope $= 1$ and $y = 0$ when $x = b$. Hence

$$[y = x]^{\alpha} = [y = x-b],$$

so that $$(a, a)^{\alpha} = (a+b, a),$$

and $$[x = a]^{\alpha} = [x = a+b].$$

Again $$[y = am]^{\alpha} = [y = am],$$

and $$(a, am)^{\alpha} = (a+b, am).$$

By the argument used above, the line $y = xm$ joining $(0, 0)$ and (m) becomes the line joining $(b, 0)$ and (m), so that

$$[y = xm]^{\alpha} = [y = xm - bm].$$

But then, since (a, am) is on $y = xm$, we have $(a+b, am)$ on $y = xm - bm$, whence

$$am = (a+b)\, m - bm,$$

or $$am + bm = (a+b)\, m.$$

This proves the final condition (3).

6. Their use as coordinate systems

This theorem also has a converse:

5. *Any Veblen–Wedderburn system* **T** *may be used as the coordinate system of a translation plane with axis* ω.

We take as the points of π once more:

1. The finite points (a, b), where a and b are elements of **T**,
2. The infinite points (m), where $m \in$ **T**,
3. The point $Y = (\infty)$.

For the lines of π we take

1. ω, with the points (∞) and (m),
2. The lines $x = c$ containing (∞) and all the points (c, d),
3. The lines $y = xm + b$, containing the point (m) and $(a, am + b)$ for all $a, b \in$ **T**.

It is simple enough to verify that the axioms for a projective plane are satisfied; that a unique line joins any two distinct points, that a unique point lies on any two distinct lines, and that no three of the four points $(0, 0), (1, 1), (\infty)$ and (0) lie on one line. We need condition (4) of §5 to show that the lines $y = xr + b$ and $y = xs + c$, with $r \ne s$, intersect in a unique finite point.

We now have a Veblen–Wedderburn projective plane, and we want to show the existence of elations with centres on ω and axis ω.

Now the mapping of finite points given by

$$(x, y)^\beta = (x + r, y + s),$$

for fixed r and s, transforms the finite lines thus:

$$[x = c]^\beta = [x = r + c]$$

and $$[y = xm + b]^\beta = [y = xm - rm + s + b].$$

In this last transformation we are, of course, making use of condition (3) of §5.

Since the lines $x = c$ are transformed into lines $x = r + c$, the point (∞) is a fixed point, and since lines $y = xm + b$ are transformed into lines with the same slope, all points (m) on ω are fixed points. To show that the joins of corresponding points P and P^β all pass through the same point on ω, so that β is an elation, we suppose that $y = xm + b$ is the equation of the line joining

$$P = (p, q) \quad \text{and} \quad P^\beta = (p+r, q+s).$$

Then
$$q = pm + b$$

and
$$q + s = (p+r)m + b.$$

Making use of conditions (1) and (3) of § 5, these equations give us

$$s = rm.$$

Now, if $s = rt$, we have
$$rt = rm,$$

and since, by condition (2), multiplication is a loop, we must have $m = t$.

Hence the join PP^β meets ω at the fixed point (t), and we have shown that π is a translation plane with axis ω.

7. Translation planes for a pencil of lines

In this section we investigate the structure of a projective plane which is a translation plane with respect to more than one line.

6. *A plane π is a translation plane for every line passing through the point $Y = (\infty)$ if, and only if:*

1. *Its finite lines are given by the linear equations*

$$x = c \quad \text{and} \quad y = xm + b,$$

and the coordinates satisfy the following rules:

2. *Addition is an Abelian group.*

3. $(a+b)m = am + bm.$

4. $a(s+t) = as + at.$

5. *Each $a \neq 0$ has an inverse a^{-1} such that $a^{-1}a = aa^{-1} = 1$.*

6. $a^{-1}(ab) = b.$

If π is a translation plane for every line through $Y = (\infty)$, it is a translation plane, in particular, for the line ω, and so by § 5, Theorem 4 we know that the linearity conditions are satisfied, and that the coordinates are a Veblen–Wedderburn system. This gives conditions (2) and (3) of the theorem. Although multiplication is a loop, we cannot prove condition (5) on the basis of the coordinates being a Veblen–Wedderburn system since we have no associative law for multiplication. Hence conditions (4), (5) and (6) are new, and have to be proved.

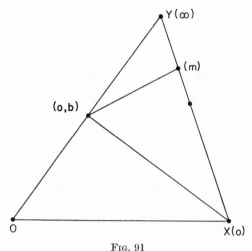

FIG. 91

Consider the elation with $Y = (\infty)$ as centre, $x = 0$ as axis, which maps the point $X = (0)$ on the point (m). If this elation is called α, we have

$$(0)^\alpha = (m).$$

Since all points on $x = 0$ are fixed points,

$$(0, b)^\alpha = (0, b).$$

Lines through X are mapped on to lines through (m), so that

$$[y = b]^\alpha = [y = xm + b].$$

Lines through Y are unchanged. Hence

$$[x = a]^\alpha = [x = a].$$

Therefore

$$(a, b)^\alpha = (a, am + b),$$

which gives the mapping for any finite point.

In particular

$$(1, t)^\alpha = (1, m + t),$$

and

$$(0, 0)^\alpha = (0, 0),$$

whence

$$[y = xt]^\alpha = [y = x(m + t)].$$

But

$$(a, at)^\alpha = (a, am + at),$$

10

and since (a, at) is on $y = xt$, the point $(a, am + at)$ is on $y = x(m+t)$, whence

$$am + at = a(m + t),$$

which proves the distributive law (4).

To prove both conditions (5) and (6), let β denote the elation with centre $(0, 0)$ and axis $x = 0$ which maps (0) on $(-1-a, 0)$. Here

$$(0)^\beta = (-1-a, 0),$$

and since all points on $x = 0$ are fixed,

$$(0, 1+a)^\beta = (0, 1+a).$$

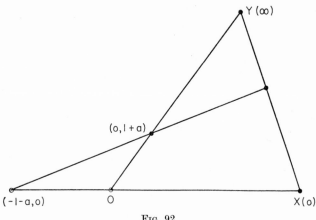

Fig. 92

The line $y = b + ab$ meets the axis of β at $(0, b+ab)$, and is transformed into the line joining $(-1-a, 0)$ to $(0, b+ab)$. If this line is $y = xm + p$, we have the equations

$$b + ab = p,$$

$$0 = (-1-a)m + b + ab.$$

Using condition (3), we can write this last equation as

$$0 = (-1-a)m + (1+a)b.$$

Clearly we can take $m = b$, since condition (3) gives

$$0q = 0 = (p-p)q = pq + (-p)q,$$

so that, since addition forms a group, we may write, in general,

$$(-p)q = -(pq).$$

Hence
$$[y = b+ab]^\beta = [y = xb+b+ab],$$

and when $b = 1$, we have
$$[y = 1+a]^\beta = [y = x+1+a].$$

Again
$$[y = x(1+a)]^\beta = [y = x(1+a)],$$

since lines through $(0,0)$ are unchanged. Hence the point $(1, 1+a)$, which lies on both the lines just considered, $y = 1+a$ and $y = x(1+a)$, is mapped on the point common to $y = x+1+a$ and $y = x(1+a)$. If the x-coordinate of this point be d, the y-coordinate is $d+1+a$, and $d+1+a = d(1+a)$, from the second equation. The two lines have the same slope if $a = 0$, so we must assume that $a \neq 0$, and we have
$$(1, 1+a)^\beta = (d, d+1+a),$$

where
$$d(1+a) = d+1+a \quad (a \neq 0).$$

Since
$$(\infty)^\beta = (\infty),$$

our last result shows that
$$[x = 1]^\beta = [x = d].$$

We saw that
$$[y = b+ab]^\beta = [y = xb+b+ab],$$

and we know that
$$[y = x(b+ab)]^\beta = [y = x(b+ab)].$$

Hence the point $(1, b+ab)$, which lies on the two lines $y = b+ab$ and $y = x(b+ab)$, is mapped on the intersection of $y = xb+b+ab$ and $y = x(b+ab)$. We know that $x = 1$ is mapped on $x = d$, hence
$$(1, b+ab)^\beta = (d, d(b+ab)),$$

where we also have
$$d(b+ab) = db+b+ab.$$

This is the result we wished to obtain. We have had to assume $a \neq 0$, but since we did not wish our point $(-1-a, 0)$ to coincide with the vertex, $(0,0)$, of the elation, we must also assume that $a \neq -1$. For such an a we have shown that a d exists such that
$$d(1+a) = d+1+a,$$

and
$$d(b+ab) = db+b+ab,$$

for any b. If we put $d = u + 1$, then

$$d(1+a) = (u+1)(1+a)$$
$$= u + ua + 1 + a$$
$$= u + 1 + 1 + a,$$

using the distributive laws, from which we see that

$$ua = 1.$$

The more general equation gives:

$$d(b+ab) = (u+1)(b+ab)$$
$$= ub + u(ab) + b + ab$$
$$= db + b + ab$$
$$= ub + b + b + ab,$$

which gives $u(ab) = b.$

The distributive laws show that $(-1)(-1) = 1$ and $-1(-b) = b$, so that even if $a = -1$, the two relations we have just proved still hold, with $u = -1$.

Since $a \neq 0$ was arbitrary, if we replace it by $u \neq 0$, there is a v such that

$$vu = 1$$

and $v(ua) = a.$

Since $ua = 1$, this last equation gives $v = a$. We now have

$$au = ua = 1,$$

and, writing $u = a^{-1}$, we have proved that

$$aa^{-1} = a^{-1}a = 1$$

and, reverting to $u(ab) = b$, this becomes

$$a^{-1}(ab) = b.$$

This concludes the proof that if π is a translation plane for every line passing through $Y = (\infty)$, then the conditions $(1), \dots, (6)$ of Theorem 6 are necessary.

8. The converse theorem

We now consider the converse, and assume that the conditions $(1), \dots, (6)$ given above are valid in a plane π, and we wish to prove that π is a translation plane with respect to all lines through $Y = (\infty)$.

By §5, Theorem 4, we know that it is a translation plane for ω, and by Ch. V, §19, Theorem 26 and Theorem 27, it will be sufficient to show that π has an elation which maps ω on to some other line through $Y = (\infty)$. For π will then be a translation plane for this axis also, and therefore for all lines through Y.

The collineation chosen has centre $(0,0)$, and its axis is the join of $(0,0)$ to $Y = (\infty)$. The definition of the collineation, α, is as follows:

$$(\infty)^\alpha = (\infty),$$

$$(m)^\alpha = (1, m),$$

$$(0, b)^\alpha = (0, b).$$

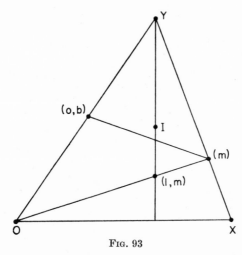

Fig. 93

This means that

$$[y = xm]^\alpha = [y = xm],$$

and we can obtain the map of the line

$$y = xm + b.$$

If its map is $$y = xm' + b',$$

we see that $b' = b$, since the new line still passes through $(0, b)$, and since it also passes through $(1, m)$,

$$m = m' + b,$$

$$m - b = m'.$$

Hence $$[y = xm + b]^\alpha = [y = x(m - b) + b].$$

The point (c, d), where $c \neq 0$, lies on the line

$$y = x(c^{-1}d),$$

using conditions (5) and (6).

The point also lies on $y = d$, and, after transformation, this line passes through $(0, d)$ and $(1, 0)$. Its equation is therefore $y = x(-d) + d$. The transform of (c, d) is therefore the intersection of $y = x(c^{-1}d)$, which is unchanged by the mapping, and $y = x(-d) + d$. If the coordinates of the point of intersection can be determined, using the conditions $(2), \ldots, (6)$, we shall have shown that the collineation we have described does exist. We have

$$y = x(c^{-1}d) = x(-d) + d,$$

and we may write, using (4),

$$x(c^{-1}d + d) = d,$$

or, using (3),

$$x[(c^{-1} + 1)d] = d.$$

If $c \neq -1$, $(c^{-1} + 1)^{-1}$ exists, by (5), and, using (6), $x = (c^{-1} + 1)^{-1}$ gives

$$(c^{-1} + 1)^{-1}[(c^{-1} + 1)d] = d,$$

so that the point

$$((c^{-1} + 1)^{-1}, (c^{-1} + 1)^{-1}(c^{-1}d))$$

is the transform of (c, d), and we have shown that with a system of coordinates satisfying the conditions $(1), \ldots, (6)$, the collineation we have described exists in π. This concludes the proof that π is a translation plane for every line through Y when the conditions $(1), \ldots, (6)$ hold.

Exercises

1. The case (c, d), where $c = -1$, has not been considered in the above. Prove that

$$(-1, d)^\alpha = (-d).$$

2. Prove the identities, using conditions $(2), \ldots, (6)$,

$$(1 + c)^{-1}(cm) = (1 + c^{-1})^{-1}m,$$
$$(1 + c)^{-1}b = (1 + c^{-1})^{-1}(-b) + b.$$

9. The Moufang identity

There are further important consequences of the conditions $(2), \ldots, (6)$ given above. We now show how to derive the Moufang identity:

7.　　　　　$$[y(zy)]x = y[z(yx)],$$

which, when $z = 1$, reduces to

8.
$$(yy)\, x = y(yx),$$

which is called the *left alternative law*.

The method given is due to R. H. Bruck. Write

$$[y^{-1} - (y + z^{-1})^{-1}]\,[y(zy) + y] = t,$$

where the values $y = 0$ and $y = -z^{-1}$ are excluded. On multiplying on the left by $y + z^{-1}$, we have

$$(y + z^{-1})\, t = (y + z^{-1})\,[(zy) + 1 - (y + z^{-1})^{-1} y(zy) - (y + z^{-1})^{-1} y],$$

using conditions (4) and (6). Further multiplication gives

$$(y + z^{-1})\, t = y(zy) + y + y + z^{-1} - y(zy) - y = y + z^{-1},$$

using (3) and (6). It follows from (5) that $t = 1$, so that

$$y^{-1} - (y + z^{-1})^{-1} \quad \text{and} \quad y(zy) + y$$

are inverses. Hence, for any x,

$$[y^{-1} - (y + z^{-1})^{-1}]\,[[y(zy)]\, x + yx] = x,$$

using (6) and (3).

Now write

$$[y^{-1} - (y + z^{-1})^{-1}]\,[y[z(yx)] + yx] = w.$$

We now find that

$$\begin{aligned}
(y + z^{-1})\, w &= (y + z^{-1})\,[z(yx) + x] - y[z(yx)] - yx \\
&= y[z(yx)] + yx + yx + z^{-1}x - y[z(yx)] - yx \\
&= yx + z^{-1}x = (y + z^{-1})\, x.
\end{aligned}$$

Hence, using (5), we must have $w = x$. Comparing the expressions for w and x, it follows that

$$[y(zy)]\, x = y[z(yx)].$$

This is called the Moufang identity. It is clearly valid also for the excluded values, $y = 0$ and $y = -z^{-1}$, and so holds without exception. If we put $z = 1$, we obtain the identity

$$(yy)\, x = y(yx).$$

10. Moufang planes

We now move on to planes which are translation planes for every line in the plane. These are called Moufang planes, after Ruth Moufang, who first studied them (see Hall [**9**]). We shall see that the coordinates in a Moufang plane belong to an *alternative division ring,* and we list the properties of such a ring:

1. Addition is an Abelian group.
2. $(a+b)m = am+bm$.
3. $a(s+t) = as+at$.
4. Each $a \neq 0$ has an inverse a^{-1} satisfying $a^{-1}a = aa^{-1} = 1$.
5. $a^{-1}(ab) = b$.
6. $(ba)a^{-1} = b$.
7. $a(ab) = (aa)b, \quad (ba)a = b(aa)$.

9. *A plane is a Moufang plane if, and only if, every ternary ring is linear, and is also an alternative division ring.*

From the previous theorem, § 7, Theorem 6, we see that if a plane is a Moufang plane then every ternary ring is linear, and we also see that conditions $(1), \ldots, (5)$ as stated above are satisfied. All we have to prove is condition (6), since from $(ba)a^{-1} = b$ we shall be able to deduce the right alternative law

$$(ba)a = b(aa)$$

in just the same way that we deduced the left alternative law

$$a(ab) = (aa)b$$

from $a^{-1}(ab) = b$.

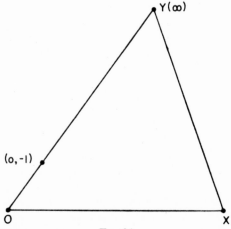

Fɪɢ. 94

We consider the elation with axis $y = 0$ and centre $(0,0)$ such that

$$(\infty)^{\alpha} = (0, -1),$$

and obtain the transform of the line $y = 1-ab$ in two ways.

We have
$$(1,0)^\alpha = (1,0)$$
and, simply,
$$[x = 1]^\alpha = [y = x-1].$$
Hence, since
$$[y = x(1-ab)]^\alpha = [y = x(1-ab)],$$
$$(1, 1-ab)^\alpha = ((ab)^{-1}, (ab)^{-1}-1),$$
on solving the equations $y = x-1$ and $y = x(1-ab)$.

Again
$$(a,0)^\alpha = (a,0)$$
and
$$[x = a]^\alpha = [y = xa^{-1}-1].$$
Since
$$[y = x(a^{-1}-b)]^\alpha = [y = x(a^{-1}-b)],$$
the point $(a, 1-ab)$ is transformed into the intersection of the lines $y = xa^{-1}-1$ and $y = x(a^{-1}-b)$. These lines intersect where
$$xa^{-1}-1 = xa^{-1}-xb,$$
and $x = b^{-1}$, $y = b^{-1}a^{-1}-1$. Hence
$$(a, 1-ab)^\alpha = (b^{-1}, b^{-1}a^{-1}-1).$$
Since
$$(0)^\alpha = (0),$$
$$[y = 1-ab]^\alpha = [y = b^{-1}a^{-1}-1],$$
and our previous work shows that
$$[y = 1-ab]^\alpha = [y = (ab)^{-1}-1].$$
Hence we have proved that
$$(ab)^{-1} = b^{-1}a^{-1}.$$
This gives, since
$$b^{-1} = a(a^{-1}b^{-1}),$$
$$b = (b^{-1})^{-1} = [a(a^{-1}b^{-1})]^{-1}$$
$$= (a^{-1}b^{-1})^{-1}a^{-1}$$
$$= (ba)a^{-1}.$$

This proves that in a Moufang plane the coordinates satisfy the above laws for an alternative division ring.

11. Construction via an alternative division ring

Conversely, suppose we are given an alternative division ring. We construct a plane with these coordinates, and see, by §7, Theorem 6, that the plane is a translation plane for every line passing through $Y = (\infty)$. Hence, by Ch. V, §19, Corollary, Theorem 26, if we can find a line of the plane, not passing through $Y = (\infty)$, for which π is a translation plane, then the plane is a translation plane for every line in it. Any homology which moves $Y = (\infty)$ will do, by Ch. V, §19, Theorem 27, and a simple one, with centre (-1) and axis $y = x$, is given by

$$(a, b)^\alpha = (b, a),$$

$$(0)^\alpha = (\infty),$$

$$(m)^\alpha = (m^{-1}), \quad m \neq 0,$$

$$[x = c]^\alpha = [y = c],$$

and $\qquad [y = xm + b]^\alpha = [y = xm^{-1} - bm^{-1}], \quad m \neq 0.$

This homology is an involution. It converts the elation, centre $Y = (\infty)$ and axis $x = 0$, say, into an elation centre $X = (0)$ and axis $y = 0$. It also converts the elation centre $(0, 0)$ and axis $x = 0$ into an elation centre $(0, 0)$ and axis $y = 0$. Hence the plane is also a translation plane for $y = 0$, and it is therefore a Moufang plane.

Far more can be said about Moufang planes, but this must be left to other texts. The reader may consult Hall [**9**]. What can be mentioned here is that if a plane is a translation plane for two distinct lines then it is a translation plane for every line, that is, a Moufang plane. Hence the law $(ba)\,a^{-1} = b$ should be a consequence of the preceding laws $(1), \dots, (5)$ at the beginning of §10.

12. Desarguesian planes

We now move on to Desarguesian planes, and first consider the case where the Desargues theorem is valid for a given centre $X = (0)$ and a given axis of perspective $x = 0$. We saw the connection with the existence of homologies in Ch. V, §17.

10. *The following conditions in a plane π are equivalent:*

1. *π is (X, OY)-transitive, that is π has all homologies with centre $X = (0)$ and axis $x = 0$.*

2. *In the ternary ring for π based on the four points X, Y, O, I, we have*

(a) $\mathbf{T}[x, m, b] = xm + b$, *and*

(b) *Multiplication is a group.*

Assuming that π is (X, OY)-transitive, we set up our coordinate system as in §1 and consider the homology α with axis $x = 0$ and centre $X = (0)$ which maps the point (m) on $\omega = XY$ on to the point (1), also on ω. We have

$$(0,0)^\alpha = (0,0),$$

$$(m)^\alpha = (1),$$

whence $\qquad\qquad [y = xm]^\alpha = [y = x].$

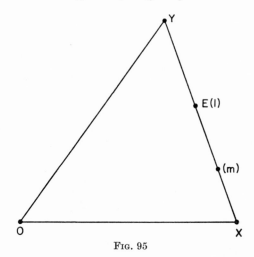

Fig. 95

Since lines through X are unaltered,

$$[y = am]^\alpha = [y = am],$$

so that $\qquad\qquad (a, am)^\alpha = (am, am).$

Since $\qquad\qquad (\infty)^\alpha = (\infty),$

$$[x = a]^\alpha = [x = am],$$

and since $\qquad\qquad [y = c]^\alpha = [y = c],$

$$(a, c)^\alpha = (am, c).$$

Also $\qquad\qquad (0, b)^\alpha = (0, b),$

and $\qquad\qquad (m)^\alpha = (1),$

therefore the line

$$y = \mathbf{T}[x, m, b]$$

which joins $(0, b)$ to (m) becomes the line joining $(0, b)$ to (1), which is

$$y = x + b.$$

Hence if (a, c) is on $y = \mathbf{T}[x, m, b]$, we have (am, c) on $y = x + b$. Thus

$$c = \mathbf{T}[a, m, b]$$

implies $\qquad\qquad c = am + b,$

whence $\qquad\qquad \mathbf{T}[a, m, b] = am + b,$

which is the linearity condition $(2, \mathrm{a})$ of Theorem 10.

The homology determined by $(m)^\alpha = (1)$ maps $(a, 1)$ on $(am, 1)$, and in particular

$$(1, 1)^\alpha = (m, 1).$$

Let β be the homology determined by

$$(n)^\beta = (1).$$

Then $\qquad\qquad [(1, 1)^\alpha]^\beta = (m, 1)^\beta = (mn, 1),$

and $\qquad\qquad [(a, 1)^\alpha]^\beta = (am, 1)^\beta = ((am)\, n, 1).$

Now, since π possesses all homologies with centre $X = (0)$ and axis $x = 0$, the product $\alpha\beta$ is an homology with centre $X = (0)$ and axis $x = 0$. As such, it is determined by the mapping of any one point. We saw that $(m)^\alpha = (1)$ involved $(1, 1)^\alpha = (m, 1)$, so that this second mapping determines the homology and leads to the first. Hence, since

$$[(1, 1)^\alpha]^\beta = (mn, 1),$$

we can say that the homology $\alpha\beta$ is determined by

$$(mn)^{\alpha\beta} = (1).$$

But this leads to

$$(a, 1)^{\alpha\beta} = (a(mn), 1).$$

Hence

$$(am)\, n = a(mn),$$

which is the associative law for multiplication.

Since multiplication is already a loop, by its definition, the associative law is all that need be added to make multiplication a group. This proves that condition (1) leads to condition (2).

Now suppose that we know that the ternary ring based on X, Y, O, I is linear, and that multiplication is a group. We want to demonstrate the existence of all possible homologies with centre $X = (0)$ and axis $x = 0$.

For fixed $m_0 \neq 0$ the following is an homology α in π:

$$(0)^\alpha = (0),$$
$$(\infty)^\alpha = (\infty),$$
$$(m)^\alpha = (m_0^{-1} m),$$
$$(a, b)^\alpha = (a m_0, b).$$

This gives

$$[x = a]^\alpha = [x = a m_0],$$
$$[y = xm + b]^\alpha = [y = x(m_0^{-1} m) + b].$$

As m_0 ranges over all values in the ternary ring, we obtain all homologies with centre $X = (0)$ and axis $x = 0$. Hence conditions (2) imply (1).

13. Construction via associative division rings

We have not yet reached the stage where π can be coordinatized by an associative division ring, but we are about to do so. In some treatments (Hodge and Pedoe [11]) the Desargues theorem is assumed to hold in general in π, but here we are more restrictive. We now prove

11. *The plane π can be coordinatized by an associative division ring if the following special cases of the Desargues theorem hold:*

1. *The linearity condition for any three distinct axes not through one point, and*

2. *The general theorem for one axis $X_1 Y_1$ and one centre O_1 not on the axis.*

If this is the case, the Desargues theorem holds throughout π.

From condition (1) the plane is a Moufang plane and from (2) we find, by § 12, Theorem 10, that for one particular choice of a quadrangle X_1, Y_1, O_1, I_1 from which a ternary ring **T** is determined for π, we have

$$\mathbf{T}[x, m, b] = xm + b,$$

both distributive laws hold, addition is a group, and so is multiplication. The coordinates therefore satisfy the laws for an associative division ring.

It remains only to show that the Desargues theorem holds throughout π. If the centre of perspective lies on the axis, this is certainly true, since π has all possible elations. If the centre is O_2, and X_2, Y_2 are distinct points on the axis, which is now assumed not to pass through O_2, the theorem will be true, by Ch. V, § 19, Theorem 27, if we can show that, by a product of elations, we can obtain a collineation α such that

$$(X_2)^\alpha = X_1,$$

$$(Y_2)^\alpha = Y_1,$$

$$(O_2)^\alpha = O_1,$$

where O_1 is the vertex, and X_1, Y_1 are distinct points on the axis of the collineation given by (2). This mapping is more than we need to prove the Desargues theorem, but it will provide further information about the associative division ring $\mathbf{T}$.

Assuming that this mapping theorem has been proved, and we do prove it later, as §16, Theorem 13, it follows that the Desargues theorem is true for any vertex and axis in π.

14. Planes transitive on quadrangles

But we also have:

12. *Given the conditions of the previous theorem, the collineation group for the plane π is transitive on quadrangles, and every ternary ring for π is the same associative division ring.*

First of all we show that any quadrangle X_2, Y_2, O_2, I_2 can be mapped on the quadrangle X_1, Y_1, O_1, I_1, in this order, where O_1 is the vertex, and X_1, Y_1 distinct points on the axis of the Desargues configuration given by (2) of the preceding theorem.

Assuming §16, Theorem 13, we can find a collineation, which is a product of elations, mapping X_2, Y_2, O_2 on X_1, Y_1, O_1 respectively. Let this collineation map I_2 on the point I^*. Then I^* does not lie on any side of the triangle formed by X_1, Y_1, O_1. With reference to the coordinate system based on X_1, Y_1, O_1, I_1, which we know is an associative division ring, by the previous theorem, the point I^* is a finite point with coordinates (a, b), say, where $a \neq 0$, $b \neq 0$. The collineation β now given fixes X_1, Y_1, O_1, and maps (a, b) on $I_1 = (1, 1)$:

$$(x, y)^\beta = (xa^{-1}, yb^{-1}),$$

$$(m)^\beta = (amb^{-1}),$$

$$(\infty)^\beta = (\infty).$$

The corresponding mapping for lines is

$$[y = xm + p]^\beta = [y = x(amb^{-1}) + pb^{-1}],$$

$$[x = c]^\beta = [x = ca^{-1}].$$

If we follow the collineation which maps X_2, Y_2, O_2, I_2 on X_1, Y_1, O_1, I^* respectively by the collineation β, we have a collineation which maps X_2, Y_2, O_2, I_1 on X_1, Y_1, O_1, I_1.

It follows from this that the collineation group of π is transitive on quadrangles. For if

$$[X_2, Y_2, O_2, I_2]^\gamma = [X_1, Y_1, O_1, I_1],$$

and $$[X_3, Y_3, O_3, I_3]^\delta = [X_1, Y_1, O_1, I_1],$$

then the collineation $\gamma\delta^{-1}$ maps the quadrangle X_2, Y_2, O_2, I_2 on the quadrangle X_3, Y_3, O_3, I_3.

15. Isomorphism between rings

Finally, we deduce that every ternary ring for π is the same associative division ring. We have set up such a ring with the aid of the quadrangle X_1, Y_1, O_1, I_1. Then the ternary ring set up with the quadrangle X_2, Y_2, O_2, I_2 is isomorphic to this associative division ring. For under the collineation which maps the second quadrangle on the first, suppose that the point (a_2, a_2) of $O_2 I_2$ is mapped on the point (a_1, a_1) of $O_1 I_1$. Then if we set up the mapping between the respective coordinate rings:

$$a_2 \to a_1,$$

$$(0)_2 \to (0)_1,$$

$$(1)_2 \to (1)_1,$$

where the zero and unity refer to the respective systems, we must have

$$\mathbf{T}_2[a_2, m_2, b_2] \to \mathbf{T}_1[a_1, m_1, b_1],$$

since all the operations of the respective ternary rings are derived from lines based on the vertices of the respective quadrangles, and the mapping is a collineation.

The converse is clear. If two isomorphic ternary rings $\mathbf{T}_1$ and $\mathbf{T}_2$ coordinatize the same projective plane π, then the mapping

$$(a_2, b_2) \to (a_1, b_1),$$

where $a_2 \to a_1$ and $b_2 \to b_1$ under the ring isomorphism, is a collineation, since the points on the line

$$y_2 = \mathbf{T}_2[x_2, m_2, b_2]$$

are mapped onto the points of the line

$$y_1 = \mathbf{T}_1[x_1, m_1, b_1].$$

16. A theorem on the mapping of triangles

We must now prove:

13. *If π is a translation plane for every line, and thus possesses all possible elations, there is a collineation made up of a product of these elations which maps any proper triangle O, X, Y, in order, on any other proper triangle O', X', Y', in order.*

We naturally assume that the triads are not identical. The three respective sides cannot therefore coincide with each other. We may assume, then, that $XY \neq X'Y'$. If we had $Y' \in XY$, we apply to O', X', Y' the elation with centre X' and axis $\neq X'Y'$ which maps Y' on a point $\notin XY$. If this elation be β, so that

$$[O', X', Y']^\beta = [O'', X'', Y''],$$

where $Y'' \notin XY$, and if we can find α such that

$$[O, X, Y]^\alpha = [O'', X'', Y''],$$

then the collineation $\alpha\beta^{-1}$ will map O, X, Y on O', X', Y'.

We may assume, therefore, that $XY \neq X'Y'$ and $Y' \notin XY$. We also have $X' \notin XY$, since we could not have both X' and Y' on XY initially, since $XY \neq X'Y'$, and the elation which moved Y' off XY left X' unchanged. If, originally, $X' \in XY$, but $Y' \notin XY$, we argue as above, interchanging the roles of X' and Y'. Now let $C = XX' \cap YY'$, and let l be the line joining $XY \cap X'Y'$ to C. We have $Y, Y' \neq C$, since neither X' nor Y' lies on XY, and for the same reasons neither Y nor Y' is on l. Now let α be the elation with centre C and axis l determined by the mapping $Y^\alpha = Y'$. Then since $X'Y'$ and XY meet on l, and C, X, X' are collinear, $X^\alpha = X'$.

Since neither O' nor O^α lies on $X'Y' = (XY)^\alpha$, there is a $(C', X'Y')$-elation β, where C' is chosen on $X'Y'$ so that $(O^\alpha)^\beta = O'$. The collineation $\alpha\beta$ now maps O on O', X on X' and Y on Y'.

17. Pappus and commutativity

We have now seen that if certain cases of the Desargues theorem hold in our projective plane π, the coordinate ring derived from any quadrangle O, X, Y, I is the same *associative division ring, field,* or *skew field,* whichever term we prefer to use. We do not know whether multiplication in this field is commutative or not, but our final theorem in this chapter is:

14. *The coordinate field attached to π is commutative if, and only if, the Pappus theorem holds in π.*

We have three distinct points A, B, C on one line, and three distinct points A', B', C' on another line, and none of the points is at the intersection O of the two lines. We also write $A = X$, $A' = Y$, and put $AC' \cap A'B = I$. If we coordinatize the plane with respect to X, Y, O, I, we can take

$$A = (0), \quad B = (1,0), \quad C = (m,0),$$

and
$$A' = (\infty), \quad B' = (0,n), \quad C' = (0,1),$$

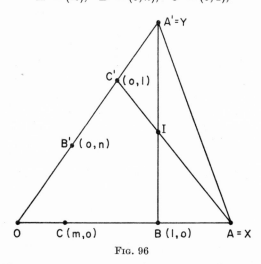

FIG. 96

where neither m nor n is zero. We find the coordinates of the intersections of the cross-joins, and investigate the condition for the three points $AB' \cap A'B$, $BC' \cap B'C$ and $CA' \cap C'A$ to be collinear.

The line AB' is $y = n$, and the line $A'B$ is $x = 1$, so that $AB' \cap A'B = (1, n)$.

The line AC' is $y = 1$, and the line $A'C$ is $x = m$, so that $AC' \cap A'C = (m, 1)$.

The line BC' is $y = -x+1$, and the line $B'C$ is the join of $(0, n)$ and $(m, 0)$, and is therefore $xm^{-1} + yn^{-1} = 1$, or $y = -xm^{-1}n + n$. This meets $y = -x+1$ where

$$0 = x(1 - m^{-1}n) + n - 1,$$

so that $x = (1-n)(1-m^{-1}n)^{-1}$, $y = 1 - (1-n)(1-m^{-1}n)^{-1}$.

We find the equation of the line joining the two points $(1, n)$ and $(m, 1)$. This is found to be

$$y = -x(n-1)(m-1)^{-1} + (n-1)(m-1)^{-1} + n,$$

11

or
$$y(m-1) = -x(n-1)+(n-1)+n(m-1),$$

that is
$$y(m-1) = -x(n-1)+nm-1.$$

The condition that this line contains the third point, so that the Pappus theorem holds, is:

$$[1-(1-n)(1-m^{-1}n)^{-1}](m-1)$$
$$= nm-1-(1-n)(1-m^{-1}n)^{-1}(n-1),$$

or
$$m-nm = (1-n)(1-m^{-1}n)^{-1}(m-n),$$

or
$$(1-n)m = (1-n)(1-m^{-1}n)^{-1}(m-n).$$

This gives
$$m = (1-m^{-1}n)^{-1}(m-n),$$
$$(1-m^{-1}n)m = m-n,$$
$$m-m^{-1}nm = m-n,$$
$$m^{-1}nm = n,$$
$$nm = mn.$$

All the steps taken in simplification are reversible, so that we have proved the equivalence of the Pappus theorem with the commutativity of multiplication.

We also know that if the Pappus theorem holds, so does the Desargues theorem (Ch. II, §8, Th. 7), and we can therefore say:

15. *If the Pappus theorem holds in π, the coordinate ring is a commutative field.*

18. A word to the reader

The reader will have noticed that in setting up a coordinate system in the projective plane π we introduced the first multiplication operation by means of a line through the point O, and we took the equation of the line to be $y = xm$. We could equally well have taken the equation to be $y = mx$, and with consequential changes the whole of this chapter is still valid. The equations of our lines, if the plane is Desarguesian, then become $y = mx+b$ instead of $y = xm+b$. The skew field obtained in the Desarguesian case with the one definition is, of course, isomorphic to the skew field obtained with the other definition, the mapping merely interchanging the order of multiplication.

In our next chapter, where we introduce homogeneous coordinates, we shall assume, merely as a matter of convenience, that the skew field has been obtained using the second form for the equation of a line.

We have concentrated, in this chapter, on finding sufficient conditions, in terms of the Desargues theorem, for a plane to be coordinatized by various types of algebraic structure. In §13, Theorem 11, we found the conditions for the structure to be a skew field. It is naturally important to obtain necessary conditions for this theorem to hold. We are interested in the theorem that *the Desargues theorem holds in any projective plane coordinatized by means of a skew field.*

For convenience, we prove this theorem, after homogeneous coordinates have been introduced, as Theorem 13, §16 of Ch. VII.

CHAPTER VII

HOMOGENEOUS COORDINATES AND COLLINEATIONS

1. Introduction of homogeneous coordinates

The coordinates introduced into a projective plane in our last chapter have the disadvantage of assigning special coordinates to the points of ω, the *line at infinity*. We may overcome this in the classical way by the use of *homogeneous coordinates*, which we now discuss.

We assume that the projective plane π is Desarguesian, so that the ternary ring **T** is a skew field (Ch. VI, §13, Th. 11). We denote this skew field by the symbol K. Our fundamental quadrangle O, X, Y, I, which was used for introducing coordinates, is used for the introduction of a *vector space* **V** with a basis $(\mathbf{e}_0, \mathbf{e}_1, \mathbf{e}_2)$.

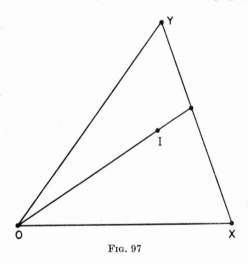

Fig. 97

This vector space consists of all vectors of the form

$$\mathbf{e}_0 \cdot x_0 + \mathbf{e}_1 \cdot x_1 + \mathbf{e}_2 \cdot x_2,$$

with the rules:

$$\sum_{i=0}^{2} \mathbf{e}_i . x_i + \sum_{i=0}^{2} \mathbf{e}_i . y_i = \sum_{i=0}^{2} \mathbf{e}_i . (x_i + y_i),$$

and

$$\left(\sum_{i=0}^{2} \mathbf{e}_i . x_i \right) . x = \sum_{i=0}^{2} \mathbf{e}_i . (x_i x).$$

The elements x_i, y_i, x, y are elements of K, and are called *scalars*.

We now set up the correspondence between the coordinates already introduced and the coordinates introduced via the vector space $\mathbf{V}$. We map the ordinary point $P = (x, y)$ on to the vector space

$$(\mathbf{e}_0 + \mathbf{e}_1 . x + \mathbf{e}_2 . y) . z,$$

where z is an arbitrary non-zero element of K. This vector-space, since z is arbitrary, is one-dimensional, and we denote it by $\mathbf{V}_P$.

Every vector $\neq \mathbf{0}$ in $\mathbf{V}_P$ is called a *coordinate vector* of P. If (x_0, x_1, x_2) are the coordinates of such a vector, we have

$$x_0 = z, \quad x_1 = xz, \quad x_2 = yz.$$

These are the *homogeneous coordinates* of P. The *non-homogeneous coordinates* (x, y) of P are related to the homogeneous coordinates (x_0, x_1, x_2) of P by the formulae:

$$x = x_1 x_0^{-1}, \quad y = x_2 x_0^{-1}.\dagger$$

In homogeneous coordinates the unit point $I = (1, 1, 1)$, and as a vector $\mathbf{e}$, we have

$$\mathbf{e} = \mathbf{e}_0 + \mathbf{e}_1 + \mathbf{e}_2.$$

The points on $\omega = XY$ have not been discussed as yet. We obtain all points on XY except Y from

$$(\mathbf{e}_1 + \mathbf{e}_2 . u) . z,$$

whilst Y itself is given by $\mathbf{e}_2 . z$.

Hence the homogeneous coordinates of points on XY are $(0, 1, u)$, but Y itself is $(0, 0, 1)$.

Our fundamental points are:

$$O = (1, 0, 0), \quad X = (0, 1, 0), \quad Y = (0, 0, 1), \quad I = (1, 1, 1),$$

and the basis vectors $\mathbf{e}_0, \mathbf{e}_1, \mathbf{e}_2$ correspond respectively to the points O, X, Y.

† We could equally well map (x, y) on to $(\mathbf{e}_0 . x + \mathbf{e}_1 . y + \mathbf{e}_2) . z$ and then
$$x = x_0 x_2^{-1}, \quad y = x_1 x_2^{-1}.$$

The mapping $P \to \mathbf{V}_P$ is now defined for all points P in π, and is a one–one mapping of the set of points of the Desarguesian plane π onto the set of one-dimensional subspaces of $\mathbf{V}$.

For a line l in π, the corresponding vector subspace $\mathbf{V}_l$ is made up of the joins of all subspaces $\mathbf{V}_P$,

$$\mathbf{V}_l = \bigcup_{P \in l} \mathbf{V}_P,$$

so that $\mathbf{V}_P \subset \mathbf{V}_l$ follows from $P \in l$.

If $l = XY$ then $\mathbf{V}_l$ is the vector subspace with the basis $\{\mathbf{e}_1, \mathbf{e}_2\}$. If $l = OX$, then $\mathbf{V}_l$ has the basis $\{\mathbf{e}_0, \mathbf{e}_1\}$, and if $l = OY$ then $\mathbf{V}_l$ has the basis $\{\mathbf{e}_0, \mathbf{e}_2\}$.

If l joins $(c, 0)$ to Y, then $\mathbf{V}_l$ has the basis $\{\mathbf{e}_0 + \mathbf{e}_1.c, \mathbf{e}_2\}$. If l joins $(0, d)$ to X, then $\mathbf{V}_l$ has the basis $\{\mathbf{e}_0 + \mathbf{e}_2.d, \mathbf{e}_1\}$. If l passes through O and is the line $y = mx$, then $\mathbf{V}_l$ has the basis $\{\mathbf{e}_0, \mathbf{e}_1 + \mathbf{e}_2.m\}$.

Finally, if l does not pass through O, X or Y, but meets OY in $(0, b)$ and XY in (m), so that its equation in non-homogeneous coordinates is $y = mx + b$, then $\mathbf{V}$ has the basis $\{\mathbf{e}_0 + \mathbf{e}_2.b, \mathbf{e}_1 + \mathbf{e}_2.m\}$. Since every two-dimensional subspace of $\mathbf{V}$ has a basis of one of the three distinct types just described, it follows that the mapping $l \to \mathbf{V}_l$ is a one–one mapping of the lines of π onto the set of the two-dimensional subspaces of $\mathbf{V}$. Two distinct one-dimensional vector subspaces can only have the zero-vector in common, so that if $\mathbf{V}_P \subset \mathbf{V}_l$ it follows that $P \in l$. We have therefore proved:†

1. *If $\mathbf{V}$ is a three-dimensional vector space over a skew field, and the one-dimensional subspaces are regarded as points, and the two-dimensional subspaces are regarded as lines, with a point lying on a line if, and only if, the corresponding one-dimensional subspace lies in the corresponding two-dimensional subspace, then a Desarguesian plane is produced, and all Desarguesian planes can be obtained in this way.*

2. Model for the relationship

A model for the relation between vector subspaces and homogeneous coordinates is easily constructed by assuming that K is the field of real numbers, and that we have the real affine three-dimensional space which consists of the points (x_0, x_1, x_2), where the x_i are all real numbers. If we take a fixed plane π in this space, then

---

† The simple direct verification that the Desargues theorem always holds in a plane coordinatized by a skew field will be found in § 16, Theorem 13.

π is intersected by a line through the origin $O = (0,0,0)$ which is not parallel to π in a point P. This point is determined by any point $Q \neq O$ on the line. If one point $\neq O$ on the line is (x_0, x_1, x_2), then any other point on the line is (cx_0, cx_1, cx_2). Hence it is reasonable to take the coordinates of P as (x_0, x_1, x_2) or (cx_0, cx_1, cx_2), where

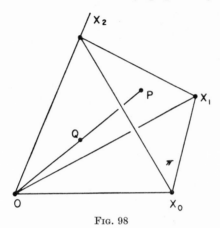

Fig. 98

c is any real number $\neq 0$, and to say that it is only the ratios $x_0 : x_1 : x_2$ which are significant. The point P is mapped on a one-dimensional space through O, and a line in π containing P is mapped on a plane through O, a two-dimensional space through O containing the line arising from P. The plane through O which is parallel to π is a definite one, and we may introduce homogeneous coordinates for the points on the *line at infinity* in π.

3. Semi-linear mappings

We return to our three-dimensional vector space $\mathbf{V}$, and define a *semi-linear mapping* λ of $\mathbf{V}$ into itself *with respect to the automorphism ϕ of K.*

If
$$(\mathbf{x}+\mathbf{y})^\lambda = \mathbf{x}^\lambda + \mathbf{y}^\lambda, \quad (\mathbf{x}.x)^\lambda = \mathbf{x}^\lambda . x^\phi,$$

where $\mathbf{x}, \mathbf{y} \in \mathbf{V}$ and $x \in K$, we say that λ is a semi-linear mapping. This definition does not depend on the dimension of $\mathbf{V}$. It is proved in the Appendix that the only automorphism of the field of real numbers is the identical automorphism, but in the field of complex numbers

$$(x+iy)^\phi = x - iy$$

is an automorphism which is not the identity. We shall find that semi-linear mappings play an important part in the study of collineations. They were introduced by Corrado Segre. If ϕ is the identical automorphism, the semi-linear mapping is a *linear* mapping.

It is easy to see that the product of a semi-linear mapping with respect to ϕ by a semi-linear mapping with respect to ψ is a semi-linear mapping with respect to $\phi\psi$. We now prove that if a semi-linear mapping λ is one–one onto (see Appendix), it does not destroy the linear dependence of vectors.

If $\mathbf{0}$ is the zero vector,

$$\mathbf{x}^\lambda = (\mathbf{x}+\mathbf{0})^\lambda = \mathbf{x}^\lambda+\mathbf{0}^\lambda,$$

from which it follows that $\mathbf{0}^\lambda = \mathbf{0}$. If, say,

$$\mathbf{x}.c+\mathbf{y}.d+\mathbf{z}.e = \mathbf{0},$$

so that the points represented by the vectors $\mathbf{x}$, $\mathbf{y}$ and $\mathbf{z}$ are collinear, then

$$(\mathbf{x}.c+\mathbf{y}.d+\mathbf{z}.e)^\lambda = \mathbf{0}^\lambda = \mathbf{0},$$

so that

$$\mathbf{x}^\lambda.c^\phi+\mathbf{y}^\lambda.d^\phi+\mathbf{z}^\lambda.e^\phi = \mathbf{0}.$$

If we assume that none of the vectors $\mathbf{x}$, $\mathbf{y}$, $\mathbf{z}$ is the zero vector, then since λ is assumed to be one–one, and $(\mathbf{0})^\lambda = \mathbf{0}$, none of the vectors $\mathbf{x}^\lambda$, $\mathbf{y}^\lambda$, $\mathbf{z}^\lambda$ is the zero vector. Again, the automorphism ϕ is by definition one–one, and $(0)^\phi = 0$, so that if none of c, d, e is 0, none of c^ϕ, d^ϕ, e^ϕ is 0. The linear relationship above is therefore non-trivial, and we have proved that collinear points are mapped on collinear points. Since λ is one–one *onto*, and therefore has an inverse (see Appendix), points which are not collinear are not mapped onto collinear points. Hence we have proved:

2. *The semi-linear transformation* λ, *which is one–one and onto, induces a collineation* $\bar\lambda$ *of the plane* π.

The relationship between λ and $\bar\lambda$ is one we now develop.

4. Semi-linear transformations and induced collineations

It is clear that if the semi-linear transformation λ induces the collineation $\bar\lambda$, and λ' induces $\bar{\lambda'}$, then $\lambda\lambda'$ induces the collineation $\bar{\lambda\lambda'}$. Hence

$$\bar{\lambda\lambda'} = \bar\lambda\bar{\lambda'},$$

so that the mapping $\lambda \to \bar\lambda$ is a *homomorphism* of the group which consists of the invertible semi-linear mappings of $\mathbf{V}$ into itself, into the group of collineations of π (see Appendix).

That the invertible semi-linear mappings form a group is a special case of a theorem for all invertible mappings (see Appendix), "invertible" being equivalent to "one–one, onto". We prove:

3. $\bar{\lambda} = \bar{\lambda}'$ *if, and only if, there is a* $c \neq 0$ *in* K *such that*

$$\mathbf{x}^\lambda = \mathbf{x}^{\lambda'} . c$$

for all $\mathbf{x} \in \mathbf{V}$.

Since the invertible semi-linear mappings form a group, it is sufficient to prove the theorem for the case $\lambda' = 1$ (the identical mapping). If $\mathbf{x}^\lambda = \mathbf{x} . c$, it is evident that the induced collineation $\bar{\lambda} = 1$.

We suppose, conversely, that $\bar{\lambda} = 1$. Then to every $\mathbf{x} \in \mathbf{V}$ there is a c, *which depends on* x, in K such that

$$\mathbf{x}^\lambda = \mathbf{x} . c.$$

To make this dependence clear, we write

$$\mathbf{x}^\lambda = \mathbf{x} . c(\mathbf{x}).$$

From the equation

$$(\mathbf{x} + \mathbf{y})^\lambda = \mathbf{x}^\lambda + \mathbf{y}^\lambda$$

we have

$$(\mathbf{x} + \mathbf{y}) . c(\mathbf{x} + \mathbf{y}) = \mathbf{x} . c(\mathbf{x}) + \mathbf{y} . c(\mathbf{y}).$$

If $\mathbf{x}$ and $\mathbf{y}$ are linearly independent, we deduce from

$$\mathbf{x} . [c(\mathbf{x} + \mathbf{y}) - c(\mathbf{x})] + \mathbf{y} . [c(\mathbf{x} + \mathbf{y}) - c(\mathbf{y})] = \mathbf{0}$$

that $c(\mathbf{x}) = c(\mathbf{x} + \mathbf{y}) = c(\mathbf{y})$. If $\mathbf{x}$ and $\mathbf{y}$ are dependent and $\neq \mathbf{0}$ we can always find a vector $\mathbf{z} \in \mathbf{V}$ such that $\mathbf{x}$ and $\mathbf{z}$ (and therefore also $\mathbf{y}$ and $\mathbf{z}$) are linearly independent. We then have

$$c(\mathbf{x}) = c(\mathbf{z}) = c(\mathbf{y}).$$

Hence for two arbitrary vectors $\mathbf{x}, \mathbf{y} \neq \mathbf{0}$ we have shown that $c(\mathbf{x}) = c(\mathbf{y})$. That is

$$c(\mathbf{x}) = c$$

for all $\mathbf{x} \neq \mathbf{0}$ if we put $c = c(\mathbf{y})$ for any fixed vector $\mathbf{y} \neq \mathbf{0}$. Hence

$$\mathbf{x}^\lambda = \mathbf{x} . c,$$

where $c \in K$ is independent of $\mathbf{x}$. This is also true for the zero vector, since

$$\mathbf{0}^\lambda = \mathbf{0} = \mathbf{0} . c.$$

Finally, since λ is one–one, we must have $c \neq 0$, and so the theorem is proved.

It will be noted that only the first defining property of a semi-linear mapping was used above, and that no use was made of the dimension of **V**, except to assume that the dimension $\geqslant 2$.

5. Equations for semi-linear mappings

The equations for a semi-linear mapping are easily obtained. If

$$\mathbf{x} = \mathbf{e}_0 . x_0 + \mathbf{e}_1 . x_1 + \mathbf{e}_2 . x_2,$$

$$\mathbf{x}^\lambda = \mathbf{e}_0 . x_0' + \mathbf{e}_1 . x_1' + \mathbf{e}_2 . x_2',$$

and $\mathbf{e}_k^\lambda = \mathbf{e}_0 . a_{0k} + \mathbf{e}_1 . a_{1k} + \mathbf{e}_2 . a_{2k} \quad (k = 0, 1, 2)$

then $\mathbf{x}^\lambda = \sum\limits_{j=0}^{2} \mathbf{e}_j^\lambda . x_j^\phi = \sum\limits_{i=0}^{2} \sum\limits_{j=0}^{2} \mathbf{e}_i . a_{ij} . x_j^\phi = \sum\limits_{i=0}^{2} \mathbf{e}_i . x_i'$

so that $x_i' = \sum\limits_{j=0}^{2} a_{ij} x_j^\phi \quad (i = 0, 1, 2).$

Since the semi-linear mapping is assumed to be invertible, the matrix $A = (a_{ij})$ is regular. Conversely, these equations define a semi-linear mapping (with respect to ϕ) when A is regular.

Hence, with a given basis for **V**, λ and consequently $\bar{\lambda}$ can be determined if ϕ and the regular matrix A are given.

Now suppose that the pair A, ϕ and the pair B, ψ determine the same collineation. By Theorem 3, there exists a $c \neq 0$ such that

$$\mathbf{x}^\lambda = \mathbf{x}^{\lambda'} . c.$$

This gives the equation

$$\left(\sum_{j=0}^{2} b_{ij} x_j^\psi \right) = \left(\sum_{j=0}^{2} a_{ij} x_j^\phi \right) . c \quad (i = 0, 1, 2).$$

Now, any automorphism of a field K maps not only the zero 0 on itself, but also the unity 1. Hence

$$(0)^\phi = (0)^\psi = 0,$$

$$(1)^\phi = (1)^\psi = 1,$$

and so $(1, 0, 0)^\phi = (1, 0, 0)^\psi = (1, 0, 0),$

which gives us

$$b_{00} = a_{00} c, \quad b_{10} = a_{10} c, \quad b_{20} = a_{20} c;$$

also $(0, 1, 0)^\phi = (0, 1, 0)^\psi = (0, 1, 0),$

which gives $b_{01} = a_{01} c, \quad b_{11} = a_{11} c, \quad b_{21} = a_{21} c,$

and finally
$$(0,0,1)^\phi = (0,0,1)^\psi = (0,0,1),$$
which gives
$$b_{02} = a_{02}c, \quad b_{12} = a_{12}c, \quad b_{22} = a_{22}c.$$

Hence $B = Ac$, and from the above equations
$$cx_j^\psi = x_j^\phi c$$
so that
$$x^\psi = c^{-1}x^\phi c$$

for all $x \in K$. This tells us that ψ is the product of ϕ by the *inner automorphism* of K (see Appendix)
$$y \to c^{-1}yc,$$
and we have proved:

4. *The automorphisms with respect to which λ is semi-linear are determined by $\bar\lambda$ except for an arbitrary inner automorphism.*

6. All collineations induced by semi-linear transformations

We now prove the theorem:

5. *The collineations of a projective plane in which the Desargues theorem holds are all induced by the semi-linear mappings of the space of the coordinate vectors.*

Let σ be an arbitrary collineation of π, and let $\mathbf{e}_0'$, $\mathbf{e}_1'$, $\mathbf{e}_2'$, $\mathbf{e}'$, where
$$\mathbf{e}_k' = \sum_{i=0}^{2} \mathbf{e}_i . e_{ik} \quad (k = 0, 1, 2),$$

$$\mathbf{e}' = \sum_{i=0}^{2} \mathbf{e}_i . e_i,$$

be the coordinate vectors of O^σ, X^σ, Y^σ, I^σ respectively. Since O, X, Y are not collinear, neither are O^σ, X^σ, Y^σ, and therefore $\mathbf{e}_0'$, $\mathbf{e}_1'$, $\mathbf{e}_2'$ span $\mathbf{V}$, and we can find c_0, c_1, c_2 in K such that
$$e_i = \sum_{k=0}^{2} e_{ik} c_k \quad (i = 0, 1, 2).$$

The mapping λ given by the equations

$$
\begin{bmatrix} x_0' \\ x_1' \\ x_2' \end{bmatrix} =
\begin{bmatrix} e_{00}c_0 & e_{01}c_1 & e_{02}c_2 \\ e_{10}c_0 & e_{11}c_1 & e_{12}c_2 \\ e_{20}c_0 & e_{21}c_1 & e_{22}c_2 \end{bmatrix}
\begin{bmatrix} x_0 \\ x_1 \\ x_2 \end{bmatrix}
$$

induces a collineation $\bar{\lambda}$ in π which clearly maps O, X, Y, I on O^σ, X^σ, Y^σ, I^σ respectively. Hence

$$\tau = \sigma\bar{\lambda}^{-1}$$

is a collineation with the fixed points O, X, Y and I.

If we look at our method of introducing coordinates into π (Ch. VI, §1), we see at once that

$$P^\tau = (x,y)^\tau = (x^\tau, y^\tau),$$

and, since addition and multiplication were defined with respect to lines derived from the four fundamental points,

$$(x+y)^\tau = x^\tau + y^\tau,$$

$$(xy)^\tau = x^\tau y^\tau,$$

so that τ *induces an automorphism ϕ of the skew field K defined with respect to O, X, Y, I.*

If now μ is the semi-linear mapping given by the equations

$$x_i' = x_i^\phi \quad (i = 0,1,2),$$

then $\bar{\mu}$ produces the same collineation as τ in the affine plane π_ω, so that

$$\tau = \bar{\mu}$$

and therefore

$$\sigma = \bar{\mu}\bar{\lambda} = \overline{\mu\lambda},$$

which proves the theorem.

As a corollary it follows that:

6. *$\lambda \to \bar{\lambda}$ is a homomorphism onto the collineation group of π.*

7. Projective collineations of π

We now introduce a new term, the *projective collineations* of π. These are simply *collineations* which are products of *central collineations*.

A central collineation always has a fixed point V such that V, P, P^σ are collinear, where P^σ is the transform of P. If the point P moves on a line l, the point P^σ moves on a line l^σ, and the points on l and l^σ are in perspective from V. In Ch. III, §2, we defined a *projective transformation* between the points on two given lines as a transformation which is a product of perspective transformations. If τ is a projective collineation of π it is now clear that the points on any line l are mapped by a projective transformation onto the points of a line l^τ.

We have already defined linear transformations as semi-linear transformations for which the automorphism ϕ is the identity. By §5, Theorem 4, a collineation $\bar\lambda$ is derived from a *linear* mapping λ if it is possible to derive it from a *semi*-linear mapping with respect to an inner automorphism. We now prove:

7. *The projective collineations of a Desarguesian plane are produced by linear mappings of the space of the coordinate vectors, and by no other semi-linear mappings.*

8. Central collineations and inner automorphisms

We first prove that for the semi-linear mapping λ with respect to ϕ, the automorphism ϕ is an inner automorphism if $\bar\lambda$ is a central collineation.

We assume that $\bar\lambda$ is a central collineation, so that there is a two-dimensional subspace $\mathbf{V}'$ of $\mathbf{V}$ whose one-dimensional subspaces are left fixed by λ. If we apply §4, Theorem 3 it follows that there is a scalar $c \neq 0$ such that

$$\mathbf{x}^\lambda = \mathbf{x}.c$$

for all $\mathbf{x} \in \mathbf{V}'$. From the fundamental equation

$$(\mathbf{x}.x)^\lambda = \mathbf{x}^\lambda.x^\phi$$

and the above, we find that

$$\mathbf{x}.cx^\phi = \mathbf{x}^\lambda.x^\phi = (\mathbf{x}.x)^\lambda = \mathbf{x}.xc,$$

for all $x \in K$, and since we may take $\mathbf{x} \neq \mathbf{0}$,

$$x^\phi = c^{-1}xc,$$

so that ϕ is an inner automorphism.

9. Linear mappings induce projective collineations: preliminaries

Conversely we must now prove that for every linear mapping λ the collineation $\bar\lambda$ is projective.

We remark in the first place that if two vectors $\mathbf{x}$ and $\mathbf{y}$ are fixed vectors under the linear mapping λ, so that

$$\mathbf{x}^\lambda = \mathbf{x}, \quad \mathbf{y}^\lambda = \mathbf{y},$$

then since λ is linear,

$$(\mathbf{x}.c+\mathbf{y}.d)^\lambda = \mathbf{x}.c+\mathbf{y}.d,$$

so that every vector in the subspace defined by $\mathbf{x}$ and $\mathbf{y}$ is fixed. Similarly if $\mathbf{x}$, $\mathbf{y}$ and $\mathbf{z}$ are three fixed vectors under λ, every vector in the subspace defined by $\mathbf{x}$, $\mathbf{y}$ and $\mathbf{z}$ is fixed.

We also remark that it is possible to produce a linear mapping which induces a central collineation σ with a given vertex and line of fixed points, and such that $P^\sigma = P'$, where P, P' is any given pair of points collinear with the vertex and distinct from it. In fact, the equations

$$
\begin{bmatrix} x_0' \\ x_1' \\ x_2' \end{bmatrix} = \begin{bmatrix} 1 & 0 & 0 \\ 0 & 1 & 0 \\ 0 & 0 & k \end{bmatrix} \begin{bmatrix} x_0 \\ x_1 \\ x_2 \end{bmatrix}
$$

define a central collineation with vertex $(0, 0, 1)$ and the line $x_2 = 0$ as the line of fixed points, and the point (x_0, x_1, x_2) is mapped on the point (x_0, x_1, kx_2), so that by choosing k we can map a given P on a given P', and the collineation is then uniquely determined.

The equations for an elation are also easily written down. They are

$$
\begin{bmatrix} x_0' \\ x_1' \\ x_2' \end{bmatrix} = \begin{bmatrix} 1 & 0 & ak \\ 0 & 1 & bk \\ 0 & 0 & 1 \end{bmatrix} \begin{bmatrix} x_0 \\ x_1 \\ x_2 \end{bmatrix},
$$

and the collineation has $x_2 = 0$ as a line of fixed points, and the vertex is $(a, b, 0)$. Once again the collineation is uniquely determined by the assignment of a pair of corresponding points collinear with $(a, b, 0)$ and distinct from it. In fact the point (x_0, x_1, x_2) is mapped on

$$(x_0 + akx_2, x_1 + bkx_2, x_2) = (x_0, x_1, x_2) + (a, b, 0)\, kx_2,$$

and if $x_2 \neq 0$ we can identify this point with any given point on the line joining $(a, b, 0)$ to (x_0, x_1, x_2), by a suitable choice of k.

In the above the vertices and lines of fixed points are in special relationship to O, X, Y and I, the points of the fundamental quadrangle, but since these fundamental points can be taken anywhere in π, the constructions are general ones.

10. Proof of theorem

With these preliminaries, let λ be a linear mapping of $\mathbf{V}$. We construct a linear mapping λ_0 such that

$$\mathbf{e}_0^{\lambda_0} = \mathbf{e}_0^\lambda, \quad \mathbf{x}^{\lambda_0} = \mathbf{x}$$

for all $\mathbf{x}$ in a two-dimensional subspace which does not contain either $\mathbf{e}_0$ or $\mathbf{e}_0^\lambda$. Then $\overline{\lambda}_0$ is a central collineation, and $\lambda' = \lambda\lambda_0^{-1}$ has the fixed vector $\mathbf{e}_0$. We now construct a linear mapping λ_1 such that

$$\mathbf{e}_1^{\lambda_1} = \mathbf{e}_1^{\lambda'}, \quad \mathbf{x}^{\lambda_1} = \mathbf{x}$$

for all $\mathbf{x}$ in a two-dimensional subspace which contains $\mathbf{e}_0$, but does not contain $\mathbf{e}_1$ or $\mathbf{e}_1^{\lambda'}$. Then $\bar{\lambda}_1$ is also a central collineation, and $\lambda_2 = \lambda'\lambda_1^{-1}$ has the fixed vectors $\mathbf{e}_0$ and $\mathbf{e}_1$. By the remark made above, λ_2 fixes all vectors in the subspace defined by $\mathbf{e}_0$ and $\mathbf{e}_1$, and therefore $\bar{\lambda}_2$ is a central collineation. Hence

$$\lambda_2 = \lambda'\lambda_1^{-1} = \lambda\lambda_0^{-1}\lambda_1^{-1},$$

so that

$$\lambda = \lambda_2\lambda_1\lambda_0,$$

and

$$\bar{\lambda} = \bar{\lambda}_2\bar{\lambda}_1\bar{\lambda}_0$$

is expressed as a product of central collineations. It is therefore a projective collineation.

11. Projective collineations from linear mappings

We saw above (§ 8) that a central collineation gives rise to a linear mapping, that is to a semi-linear mapping with respect to an inner automorphism ϕ, where

$$x^\phi = c^{-1}xc.$$

If ψ is the inner automorphism

$$x^\psi = d^{-1}xd,$$

then

$$(x^\phi)^\psi = d^{-1}(x^\phi)\,d$$

$$= d^{-1}(c^{-1}xc)\,d$$

$$= (cd)^{-1}x(cd),$$

so that $\phi\psi$ is also an inner automorphism. Hence the product of two (and therefore any number) of central collineations gives rise to a linear mapping. In other words, a *projective* collineation gives rise to a linear mapping. Application of the theorem just proved in § 10 produces the theorem:

8. *Every projective collineation of a Desarguesian plane can be expressed as the product of three central collineations.*

In other words, the product of any number n of central collineations can always be expressed as a product of *three* central collineations.

12. Projectivities between lines

In the above proof let us consider the effect of the projective collineation induced by λ on the points of a line l. The points of l are mapped by λ on the points of a line $l^{\bar{\lambda}}$. If

$$\bar{\lambda} = \sigma_1 \sigma_2 \ldots \sigma_n,$$

where the σ_i are central collineations, then σ_1 maps the points of l onto the points of l^{σ_1} by means of a perspective transformation. Again, σ_2 maps the points of l^{σ_1} onto the points of $l^{\sigma_1 \sigma_2}$ by means of a perspective transformation, ..., until finally σ_n maps the points of $l^{\sigma_1 \ldots \sigma_{n-1}}$ onto the points of $l^{\bar{\lambda}}$ by means of a perspective transformation. The points of $l^{\bar{\lambda}}$ are derived from the points of l by means of n perspectivities.

A perspectivity vertex V between two lines l and m can be produced by an elation vertex V and axis VQ, where $Q = l \cap m$. This elation exists, since π is assumed to be Desarguesian. Hence if l is mapped on the line q by a sequence of n perspectivities, these perspectivities can be produced by the projective transformation

$$\bar{\lambda} = \sigma_1 \sigma_2 \ldots \sigma_n,$$

where each σ_i is an elation and $q = l^{\bar{\lambda}}$.

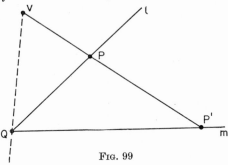

FIG. 99

Now, we reduced $\bar{\lambda}$ to a product of three central collineations,

$$\bar{\lambda} = \bar{\lambda}_2 \bar{\lambda}_1 \bar{\lambda}_0,$$

and if we take l as the line spanned by the coordinate-vectors e_0 and e_1, $\bar{\lambda}_2$ effects the identical mapping on l, and $\bar{\lambda}_1$ and $\bar{\lambda}_0$ produce perspectivities. Since the base-vectors e_0 and e_1 can always be chosen on a given line l, we have the theorem:

9. *In a Desarguesian plane any projectivity between two distinct lines may be effected by means of two perspectivities.*

This was proved by purely geometrical methods, without the use of coordinates, in Ch. III, §4, Theorem 2.

A point we have silently passed over in the construction of λ_0 and λ_1 is this: we must ensure that neither the vertex of $\overline{\lambda}_0$ nor the vertex of $\overline{\lambda}_1$ lies on the line l if we are to talk of *perspectivities*, since there is no perspectivity between two lines l and m if the vertex of perspective lies on l. This can be ensured if $l^\lambda \neq l$, but if $\overline{\lambda}$ maps l onto itself, the construction for λ_0 and for λ_1 shows that each vertex lies on l.

Hence we cannot say that a projectivity of a line onto itself can be effected by means of *two* perspectivities. Three are needed.

Another indication that two perspectivities will not do arises from the consideration that if

$$(P)\frac{V}{\overline{\wedge}}(P')\frac{U}{\overline{\wedge}}(P''),$$

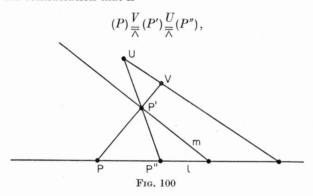

Fig. 100

using the notation of Ch. III, §1, where $P' \in m$, then the point $l \cap m$ is evidently a fixed point of the projectivity. So is the point where the line UV meets l. But there are projectivities for a suitable K which have no fixed points.

In fact, if K is the field of rational numbers, the mapping

$$\begin{bmatrix} x_0' \\ x_1' \\ x_2' \end{bmatrix} = \begin{bmatrix} 0 & 1 & 0 \\ -1 & 0 & 0 \\ 0 & 0 & 0 \end{bmatrix} \begin{bmatrix} x_0 \\ x_1 \\ x_2 \end{bmatrix}$$

or
$$x_0' = x_1, \quad x_1' = -x_0, \quad x_2' = 0$$

is a linear mapping of the line $x_2 = 0$ onto itself. For a fixed point $(x_0, x_1, 0)$,
$$x_0' = x_0 k, \quad x_1' = x_1 k \quad (k \neq 0),$$

so that
$$x_1 = x_0 k, \quad -x_0 = x_1 k.$$

12

Hence, since the field is commutative,

$$x_1 x_0 - x_0 x_1 = 0 = (x_0^2 + x_1^2) k,$$

and since $x_0^2 + x_1^2 \neq 0$, it follows that $k = 0$, which means that there is no fixed point.

13. Collineations and projective transformations: preliminaries

We saw above (§ 7) that a projective collineation induces a projective transformation on the points of any line. We now prove the converse:

10. *A collineation in a Desarguesian plane which induces a projective transformation on the points of every line is itself a projective collineation.*

We begin by modifying our proof of Ch. VI, § 14, Theorem 12, so that we can assert:

11. *The projective group of a Desarguesian plane is transitive on quadrangles.*

We recall that the products of central collineations are called *projective collineations*, and these clearly form a group, which is called the *projective group* of the plane π. We only need to modify the proof of Theorem 12 slightly, since we began by proving, in Ch. VI, § 16, Theorem 13, that any proper triangle O, X, Y can be mapped on any other proper triangle O', X', Y', in order, by a product of elations.

Assuming this result, we follow this projective collineation by a projective collineation which has O', X', Y' as united points, and maps I^*, the point which arises from I under the first projective collineation, onto the point I'. This projective collineation is constructed thus:

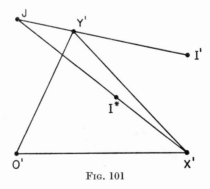

FIG. 101

Since neither I^* nor I' lies on the sides of the triangle $O'X'Y'$, the point $J = X'I^* \cap I'Y'$ does not lie on $O'X'$ or $O'Y'$. Let σ be the $(X', O'Y')$-collineation such that $(I^*)^\sigma = J$, and let τ be the $(Y', O'X')$-collineation such that $J^\tau = I'$. Then the projective collineation $\rho = \sigma\tau$ has O', X', Y' as united points and maps I^* on I'. This completes the proof of Theorem 11 above.

14. Proof of theorem

Returning to the proof of Theorem 10, let σ be the given collineation which induces projective transformations on the points of every line. If $O^\sigma = O'$, $X^\sigma = X'$, $Y^\sigma = Y'$ and $I^\sigma = I'$ we now know that we can find a *projective* collineation $\bar{\lambda}$ which also maps O, X, Y, I on O', X', Y', I' respectively. Hence $\tau = \sigma\lambda^{-1}$ has the fixed points O, X, Y and I. We consider the effect of τ on the points of the line OY.

By hypothesis σ produces a projective transformation between the points of OY and the points of $O'Y'$, and since $\bar{\lambda}$ is a projective collineation, so is $\bar{\lambda}^{-1}$, and this also produces a projective transformation between the points of $O'Y'$ and those of OY. Hence τ induces a projective transformation of OY onto itself. The fixed points of this mapping are O, Y and the point $OY \cap XI$.

We saw (§ 12) that any perspectivity between two lines can be induced by an elation, which is a central collineation. Any projectivity between the points of OY is produced by a product of perspectivities, and can therefore be produced by a product of central collineations, that is by a projective collineation of π, which we call $\bar{\mu}$. We examine the equations for μ.

We may take $\phi = 1$, and have

$$x'_i = a_{i0}x_0 + a_{i1}x_1 + a_{i2}x_2 \quad (i = 0, 1, 2).$$

Since any point $(x_0, 0, x_2)$ must be mapped on a similar point,

$$a_{10} = a_{12} = 0.$$

For points on $x_1 = 0$ we have

$$x'_0 = a_{00}x_0 + a_{02}x_2,$$

$$x'_2 = a_{20}x_0 + a_{22}x_2,$$

and $O = (1, 0, 0)$ is mapped on $(a_{00}, 0, a_{20})$. Hence $a_{20} = 0$, since O is fixed. The point $Y = (0, 0, 1)$ is mapped on $(a_{02}, 0, a_{22})$, and so

$a_{02} = 0$, since Y is fixed. Finally the point $OY \cap XI = (1,0,1)$ is mapped on $(a_{00}, 0, a_{22})$, so that $a_{00} = a_{22}$, and our equations become

$$x_0' = ax_0,$$
$$x_1' = 0,$$
$$x_2' = ax_2,$$

for points on OY.

This means that if $(0, y)$ is such a point in non-homogeneous coordinates,

$$(0, y)^\tau = (0, aya^{-1}),$$
$$y^\tau = aya^{-1}.$$

Hence τ, and therefore also σ, is represented by a semi-linear mapping with respect to an inner automorphism, so that σ is a projective collineation, which proves the theorem.

15. Change of basis

Finally, let us see what happens if we replace the fundamental quadrangle O, X, Y, I by another quadrangle O^*, X^*, Y^*, I^*. The skew field K^* we now obtain relative to the points O^*, X^*, Y^*, I^* in the Desarguesian plane π is not the same as K, but it is isomorphic to it. By Ch. VI, §15, the isomorphism of K on K^* is effected by means of a collineation σ of π.†

In order to be able to work in one and the same skew field K, we suppose the mapping σ^{-1} applied to all the elements of K^*. The homogeneous coordinates (x_0^*, x_1^*, x_2^*) obtained in this manner of a point P relative to O^*, X^*, Y^*, I^* are then merely the coordinates of $P^{\sigma^{-1}}$ relative to O, X, Y, I.

If we denote the homogeneous coordinates of P relative to O, X, Y, I by (x_0, x_1, x_2), and represent σ by the equations ($\phi = 1$):

$$x_i' = \sum_{j=0}^{2} a_{ij} x_j \quad (i = 0, 1, 2),$$

then the relationship between (x_0, x_1, x_2) and (x_0^*, x_1^*, x_2^*) is given by the equations

$$x_i = \sum_{j=0}^{2} a_{ij} x_j^* \quad (i = 0, 1, 2),$$

and this gives the equations of the transformation of coordinates induced by σ. By §7, Theorem 7 we now have the theorem:

† By §13, Theorem 11, this collineation may be assumed to be a projective collineation.

12. *It is only those transformations of coordinates of a Desarguesian plane which are induced by a projective collineation which are invoked by a change of basis for coordinate vectors.*

We may obtain this result very rapidly from the equations

$$P = \mathbf{e}_0.x_0 + \mathbf{e}_1.x_1 + \mathbf{e}_2.x_2 = \mathbf{e}_0^*.x_0^* + \mathbf{e}_1^*.x_1^* + \mathbf{e}_2^*.x_2^*,$$

$$\mathbf{e}_j^* = \sum_{i=0}^{2} \mathbf{e}_i.a_{ij} \quad (j = 0, 1, 2),$$

whence
$$\sum_{i=0}^{2} \mathbf{e}_i.x_i = \sum_{j=0}^{2} \mathbf{e}_j^*.x_j^* = \sum_{i=0}^{2} \sum_{j=0}^{2} (\mathbf{e}_i.a_{ij}).x_j^*,$$

and since $\mathbf{e}_0, \mathbf{e}_1, \mathbf{e}_2$ are linearly independent

$$x_i = \sum_{j=0}^{2} a_{ij} x_j^* \quad (i = 0, 1, 2).$$

16. Right-hand, left-hand projective number spaces

It will have been remarked that in this chapter we have regarded the coordinates

$$(x_0, x_1, x_2) \quad \text{and} \quad (x_0 k, x_1 k, x_2 k)$$

as defining the same point of π. We may say that the points of π have been mapped on those of a *right-hand projective number space*. In this space the equation of a line is of the form

$$a_0 x_0 + a_1 x_1 + a_2 x_2 = 0.$$

If we had considered the points

$$(x_0, x_1, x_2) \quad \text{and} \quad (k x_0, k x_1, k x_2)$$

to be identical, the equation of a line in this left-hand projective number space would be

$$x_0 a_0 + x_1 a_1 + x_2 a_2 = 0.$$

If K is commutative, of course, we do not distinguish between the two cases.

To conclude this chapter we prove:

13. *In a projective plane defined over any skew field K, the Desargues theorem is always true.*

Referring to Fig. 26, we assume that the vertex of perspective V, and the vertices $A, B, C,\ A', B', C'$ of the two triangles are all distinct points. Let $\boldsymbol{\epsilon}$ be the vector denoting V after homogeneous coordinates over the skew field K have been introduced. Then if

$A = \alpha$, $A' = \alpha'$, $B = \beta$, $B' = \beta'$, $C = \gamma$, $C' = \gamma'$ in this representation, we may normalize each set of vectors representing collinear points so that (Ch. VIII, §1, Th. 1)

$$\epsilon = \alpha + \alpha' = \beta + \beta' = \gamma + \gamma'.$$

Let $\rho = \beta - \gamma = \gamma' - \beta'$, $\sigma = \gamma - \alpha = \alpha' - \gamma'$, $\tau = \alpha - \beta = \beta' - \alpha'$.

Then the point represented by ρ lies on both BC and $B'C'$, and is therefore L. Similarly σ represents M and τ represents N. But

$$\rho + \sigma + \tau = \beta - \gamma + \gamma - \alpha + \alpha - \beta = \mathbf{0}.$$

Hence L, M and N are collinear.

We therefore now have the theorem (cf. Ch. VI, §13, Th. 11).

14. *A necessary and sufficient condition that a projective plane be coordinatized by a skew field is that the Desargues theorem holds throughout the plane.*

CHAPTER VIII

CROSS-RATIOS

1. Normalization of three vectors

We have seen that a triad of distinct collinear points can always be mapped on any given triad of distinct collinear points by means of a projectivity (Ch. III, §3, Th. 1). We now investigate the conditions under which a corresponding theorem holds for quadruples of collinear points. We shall associate with four distinct collinear points a class of scalars which is invariant with respect to projectivities.

We assume once more that we are in a Desarguesian plane π, and that a skew field K has been defined for π by means of a definite coordinate system. If $\mathbf{x}$, $\mathbf{y}$ are the coordinate vectors of two distinct points on a line, any other point on the line has a coordinate vector $\mathbf{z}$ where

$$\mathbf{z} = \mathbf{x}u + \mathbf{y}v \quad (u, v \in K).$$

Since the point with coordinate vector $\mathbf{z}$ is distinct from the points with coordinate vectors $\mathbf{x}$ and $\mathbf{y}$ respectively, we have $u \neq 0$ and $v \neq 0$. (There will be no confusion if we speak of "the point $\mathbf{z}$" when we mean "the point with coordinate vector $\mathbf{z}$".) Since the point $\mathbf{x}u$ is the same as the point $\mathbf{x}$ (we *absorb* the scalar u), and the point $\mathbf{y}v$ is the same as the point $\mathbf{y}$, we can write

$$\mathbf{z} = \mathbf{x} + \mathbf{y},$$

and we have proved:

1. *The coordinate vectors* $\mathbf{x}$, $\mathbf{y}$, $\mathbf{z}$ *of three distinct collinear points can be normalized, that is multiplied on the right by convenient scalars, so that* $\mathbf{z} = \mathbf{x} + \mathbf{y}$.

We note that if $\mathbf{z} = \mathbf{x} + \mathbf{y}$, and we wish to normalize $\mathbf{x}$ and $\mathbf{y}$ in any way so that $\mathbf{z}$ is still expressed as the sum of the corresponding coordinate vectors of these two points, it is necessary and sufficient that the two normalization factors be equal.

169

2. Definition of cross-ratio

We now define *the cross-ratio* of four collinear points. Let $\mathbf{x}$, $\mathbf{y}$, $\mathbf{z}$ be three distinct fixed points of a line, and let $\mathbf{t}$ be a variable point of the line. By the above, we may assume that

$$\mathbf{z} = \mathbf{x} + \mathbf{y}, \quad \mathbf{t} = \mathbf{x}u + \mathbf{y}v,$$

where u and v are in K and not both zero. Then

$$r = uv^{-1}$$

is a right-hand non-homogeneous coordinate of $\mathbf{t}$ on the line. This coordinate is not uniquely determined by the points $\mathbf{x}$, $\mathbf{y}$, $\mathbf{z}$ and $\mathbf{t}$, since, as we saw above, we can substitute for $\mathbf{x}$, $\mathbf{y}$ respectively $\mathbf{x}_1 = \mathbf{x}c$ and $\mathbf{y}_1 = \mathbf{y}c$, where $c \neq 0$ is an arbitrary scalar. We then have

$$\mathbf{t} = \mathbf{x}_1 c^{-1} u + \mathbf{y}_1 c^{-1} v = \mathbf{x}_1 u_1 + \mathbf{y}_1 v_1,$$

where $\qquad u_1 = c^{-1}u, \quad v_1 = c^{-1}v,$

so that instead of r we obtain

$$r_1 = u_1 v_1^{-1} = (c^{-1}u)(v^{-1}c) = c^{-1}rc,$$

which is an element *conjugate* to r in K (see Appendix). We denote the class of these conjugates by $\{r\}$, and write

$$\{\mathbf{x}, \mathbf{y}, \mathbf{z}, \mathbf{t}\} = \{r\},$$

calling $\{\mathbf{x}, \mathbf{y}, \mathbf{z}, \mathbf{t}\}$ the *cross-ratio* of the points $\mathbf{x}$, $\mathbf{y}$, $\mathbf{z}$, $\mathbf{t}$ *taken in this order.*

This cross-ratio is therefore a class of elements of K which is defined uniquely by the four points. The class consists of a single element if, and only if, r belongs to the *centre* of K (see Appendix).

3. Special cases

We have to allow the possibility that $\mathbf{t}$ may coincide with $\mathbf{x}$, in which case $v = 0$. We then write, formally, $r = \infty$, and assume the following properties of this symbol:

$$-\infty = \infty, \quad \infty^{-1} = 0, \quad \infty.\infty = \infty,$$

$$\infty + c = c + \infty = \infty, \quad \infty.c = c.\infty = \infty,$$

if $c \neq 0$, and we attach no meaning to the symbols $\infty.0$, $0.\infty$, ∞/∞, $\infty + \infty$.

We can now say that the class $\{r\}$ also consists of a single element if $r = \infty$.

Conversely, given $\mathbf{x}$, $\mathbf{y}$, $\mathbf{z}$ and r, the point $\mathbf{t}$ satisfying the equation

$$\{\mathbf{x}, \mathbf{y}, \mathbf{z}, \mathbf{t}\} = \{r\}$$

is given by

$$\mathbf{t} = \mathbf{x}.c^{-1}rc + \mathbf{y},$$

with $c \neq 0$ arbitrary in K, or by

$$\mathbf{t} = \mathbf{x}$$

if $r = \infty$. Hence $\mathbf{t}$ is uniquely determined if and only if r belongs to the centre of K (in particular if $r = 0$, 1 or -1) or if $r = \infty$. Hence we may say:

2. *The correspondence between the point* $\mathbf{t}$ *and* r *is one–one if, and only if, the field* K *is commutative.*

4. Effect of change of order

We now show how to calculate the cross-ratio when the order of the points $\mathbf{x}$, $\mathbf{y}$, $\mathbf{z}$, $\mathbf{t}$ is changed. We suppose that

$$\{\mathbf{x}, \mathbf{y}, \mathbf{z}, \mathbf{t}\} = \{r\} \quad (r \neq 0).$$

Since

$$\mathbf{x}.r + \mathbf{y} = (\mathbf{x} + \mathbf{y}.r^{-1})\,r,$$

we have

$$\{\mathbf{y}, \mathbf{x}, \mathbf{z}, \mathbf{t}\} = \{r^{-1}\}.$$

Since

$$\mathbf{x} + \mathbf{y} = (\mathbf{x}.r)\,r^{-1} + \mathbf{y},$$

$$\{\mathbf{x}, \mathbf{y}, \mathbf{t}, \mathbf{z}\} = \{r^{-1}\}.$$

Finally, since

$$\mathbf{x}.r + \mathbf{y} = +(-\mathbf{x})(1-r) + \mathbf{x} + \mathbf{y},$$

if we write

$$\mathbf{x}' = -\mathbf{x}, \quad \mathbf{y}' = \mathbf{x} + \mathbf{y} = \mathbf{z}, \quad \mathbf{z}' = \mathbf{y} = \mathbf{x}' + \mathbf{y}', \quad \mathbf{t}' = \mathbf{t},$$

then

$$\{\mathbf{x}', \mathbf{y}', \mathbf{z}', \mathbf{t}'\} = \{1 - r\} = \{\mathbf{x}, \mathbf{z}, \mathbf{y}, \mathbf{t}\}.$$

Applying the first two results successively, we have

$$\{\mathbf{y}, \mathbf{x}, \mathbf{t}, \mathbf{z}\} = \{\mathbf{x}, \mathbf{y}, \mathbf{z}, \mathbf{t}\},$$

so that also, since

$$\{\mathbf{x}, \mathbf{z}, \mathbf{y}, \mathbf{t}\} = \{\mathbf{z}, \mathbf{x}, \mathbf{t}, \mathbf{y}\} = \{1 - r\},$$

we have

$$\{\mathbf{x}, \mathbf{y}, \mathbf{z}, \mathbf{t}\} = \{\mathbf{y}, \mathbf{x}, \mathbf{t}, \mathbf{z}\} = \{\mathbf{z}, \mathbf{t}, \mathbf{x}, \mathbf{y}\}$$

$$= \{\mathbf{t}, \mathbf{z}, \mathbf{y}, \mathbf{x}\}.$$

We can now write down the values of the twenty-four permutations of $\{\mathbf{x}, \mathbf{y}, \mathbf{z}, \mathbf{t}\}$, and see that we have four arrangements corresponding to each of the six values

$$r, \quad r^{-1}, \quad 1-r, \quad (1-r)^{-1}, \quad 1-(1-r)^{-1}, \quad [1-(1-r)^{-1}]^{-1}.$$

The operations x^{-1} or $1-x$ applied to any element x of this set produce an element of the set. We have assumed that

$$\{1-r\} = 1-\{r\}$$

in the above, which follows at once from the definition of $\{r\}$.

5. Projective character of cross-ratio

The importance of the cross-ratio lies in its projective character. We show that if two lines l and m cut the four lines of a pencil in the points $\mathbf{x}$, $\mathbf{y}$, $\mathbf{z}$, $\mathbf{t}$ and $\mathbf{x}'$, $\mathbf{y}'$, $\mathbf{z}'$, $\mathbf{t}'$ respectively, then

$$\{\mathbf{x}, \mathbf{y}, \mathbf{z}, \mathbf{t}\} = \{\mathbf{x}', \mathbf{y}', \mathbf{z}', \mathbf{t}'\}.$$

The equations of two lines of the pencil being

$$u_1 \equiv a_0 x_0 + a_1 x_1 + a_2 x_2 = 0$$

and $\qquad u_2 \equiv b_0 x_0 + b_1 x_1 + b_2 x_2 = 0,$

any other line of the pencil may be written in the form

$$u_1 + \lambda u_2 = 0.$$

Dually, we may, of course, represent the line $u_1 = 0$ by the vector $\boldsymbol{\xi}_1 = [a_0, a_1, a_2]$, where the vectors $\boldsymbol{\xi}_1$ and $k\boldsymbol{\xi}_1$ $(k \neq 0)$ represent the same line. We may therefore take four lines of a pencil as given by $\boldsymbol{\xi}_1$, $\boldsymbol{\xi}_2$, $\boldsymbol{\xi}_3$, $\boldsymbol{\xi}_4$, where, by normalization,

$$\boldsymbol{\xi}_3 = \boldsymbol{\xi}_1 + \boldsymbol{\xi}_2 \quad \text{and} \quad \boldsymbol{\xi}_4 = t\boldsymbol{\xi}_1 + \boldsymbol{\xi}_2.$$

The cross-ratio of the four lines of the pencil is then defined to be

$$\{\boldsymbol{\xi}_1, \boldsymbol{\xi}_2, \boldsymbol{\xi}_3, \boldsymbol{\xi}_4\} = \{t\}.$$

We prove that $\qquad \{\mathbf{x}, \mathbf{y}, \mathbf{z}, \mathbf{t}\} = \{\boldsymbol{\xi}_1, \boldsymbol{\xi}_2, \boldsymbol{\xi}_3, \boldsymbol{\xi}_4\},$

and, once this has been established, it follows that

$$\{\mathbf{x}, \mathbf{y}, \mathbf{z}, \mathbf{t}\} = \{\mathbf{x}', \mathbf{y}', \mathbf{z}', \mathbf{t}'\}.$$

For a more convenient notation let us replace the points $\mathbf{x}$, $\mathbf{y}$, $\mathbf{z}$, $\mathbf{t}$ by the points $\mathbf{x}_1$, $\mathbf{x}_2$, $\mathbf{x}_3$, $\mathbf{x}_4$. If we write

$$(\boldsymbol{\xi}, \mathbf{x}) = \xi_0 x_0 + \xi_1 x_1 + \xi_2 x_2,$$

where now $\boldsymbol{\xi} = [\xi_0, \xi_1, \xi_2]$, then since the point $\mathbf{x}_i$ lies on the line $\boldsymbol{\xi}_i$, we know that

$$(\boldsymbol{\xi}_i, \mathbf{x}_i) = 0.$$

If we write
$$c = (\xi_1, x_2),$$

we know that $c \neq 0$, for if $c = 0$ the line ξ_1 would contain both the points x_1 and x_2, and the line l on which the four points x_i lie would pass through the vertex of the pencil of lines, which is contrary to hypothesis. From the preceding equations we have

$$0 = (\xi_3, x_3) = (\xi_1 + \xi_2, x_1 + x_2)$$
$$= (\xi_1, x_1) + (\xi_1, x_2) + (\xi_2, x_1) + (\xi_2, x_2)$$
$$= (\xi_1, x_2) + (\xi_2, x_1),$$

whence
$$(\xi_2, x_1) = -(\xi_1, x_2) = -c.$$

Finally
$$0 = (\xi_4, x_4) = (t\xi_1 + \xi_2, x_1 r + x_2)$$
$$= t(\xi_1, x_1) r + t(\xi_1, x_2) + (\xi_2, x_1) r + (\xi_2, x_2)$$
$$= tc - cr,$$

so that
$$t = crc^{-1},$$

and therefore
$$\{t\} = \{r\}.$$

This proves the projective nature of the cross-ratio of four collinear points.

6. Application to harmonic conjugates

We now show that the uniqueness proofs in the construction of harmonic conjugates are very simple when coordinates are used (cf. Ch. III, §8).

Let λ, μ, ν be three distinct collinear points, and let α, β be any two points collinear with ν, distinct from ν and not on the line joining λ and μ (see Fig. 102). Let ϵ and δ be respectively the intersections of the distinct lines joining λ to α and μ to β, and λ to β and μ to α. Let the line joining δ to ϵ meet the line joining λ to μ in ρ. We show that ρ is uniquely determined by λ, μ, ν, and characterized by the condition

$$\{\lambda, \mu, \nu, \rho\} = -1.$$

We can write
$$\nu = \lambda + \mu = \alpha + \beta.$$

Then the points
$$\lambda - \alpha = \beta - \mu \quad \text{and} \quad \mu - \alpha = \beta - \lambda$$

are necessarily identified with ϵ and δ respectively, since the point $\lambda - \alpha$ is on the line joining λ to α, and $\beta - \mu$ is on the line joining β to μ, and the two lines meet in ϵ. Similarly δ is the intersection of the line joining μ to α and β to λ. Again the point

$$\epsilon - \delta = (\lambda - \alpha) - (\mu - \alpha) = \lambda - \mu$$

lies on the line joining ϵ to δ and also on the line joining λ to μ.

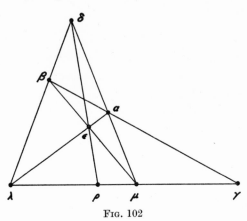

Fig. 102

We therefore have

$$\rho = \lambda - \mu.$$

Hence ρ is independent of α and β, and

$$\{\lambda, \mu, \nu, \rho\} = -1.$$

Since $\{\mu, \lambda, \nu, \rho\} = \{\lambda, \mu, \rho, \nu\} = -1$

also, the notion of harmonic conjugate enters once more.

Finally, the point ρ coincides with λ or with μ, or with ν if, and only if, the cross-ratio $\{\lambda, \mu, \nu, \rho\}$ is ∞, 0 or 1. Since −1 is neither ∞ nor 0, and

$$-1 = 1$$

if, and only if, the field K has characteristic 2, we have the theorem:

3. *The diagonal points of a quadrangle are collinear if, and only if, the field K is of characteristic* 2.

7. Cross-ratio in terms of homogeneous coordinates

It is sometimes convenient to be able to express the cross-ratio of four given points on a line in terms of the homogeneous coordinates of the points, and we now carry out the calculation. Let z_1, z_2, z_3, z_4 be four points on a line, of which the first three are distinct, and suppose that in any system of right-hand homogeneous coordinates on the line

$$\mathbf{z}_i = (x_i, y_i).$$

We wish to express the cross-ratio $\{\mathbf{z}_1, \mathbf{z}_2, \mathbf{z}_3, \mathbf{z}_4\}$ in terms of the x_i and y_j.

To do this we first determine elements a and b of K such that

$$\mathbf{z}_3 = \mathbf{z}_1 a + \mathbf{z}_2 b.$$

This leads to the equations

$$x_1 a + x_2 b = x_3, \quad y_1 a + y_2 b = y_3.$$

If $x_1 y_1 \neq 0$, we have

$$a + x_1^{-1} x_2 b = x_1^{-1} x_3,$$

$$a + y_1^{-1} y_2 b = y_1^{-1} y_3,$$

so that $\qquad b(x_1^{-1} x_2 - y_1^{-1} y_2) = x_1^{-1} x_3 - y_1^{-1} y_3.$

If we write, for short,

$$(hk) = x_h^{-1} x_k - y_h^{-1} y_k \quad (x_h y_h \neq 0),$$

we see that $\qquad b = (12)^{-1} (13)$

and similarly $\qquad a = (21)^{-1} (23).$

We note that $(12) \neq 0$, since $\mathbf{z}_1$ and $\mathbf{z}_2$ are distinct. The formulae for a and b have no meaning if $x_1 y_1 = 0$. We cannot have $x_1 = 0$ and $y_1 = 0$. If $x_1 \neq 0$, $y_1 = 0$, then $b = y_2^{-1} y_3$. If $x_1 = 0, y_1 \neq 0$, $b = x_2^{-1} x_3$. Both these values are given by the formula $b = (12)^{-1} (13)$ if we adopt the convention

$$(hk) = \begin{cases} y_h^{-1} x_k & \text{if } x_h = 0 \\ x_h^{-1} y_k & \text{if } y_h = 0. \end{cases}$$

Similarly for the value of a if $x_2 y_2 = 0$.

Continuing, we now write

$$\mathbf{z}_1 a' + \mathbf{z}_2 b' = \mathbf{z}_4,$$

and find that

$$a' = (21)^{-1} (24), \quad b' = (12)^{-1} (14).$$

If we now write $\mathbf{z}_1$ and $\mathbf{z}_2$ instead of $\mathbf{z}_1 a$ and $\mathbf{z}_2 b$, we have

$$\mathbf{z}_3 = \mathbf{z}_1 + \mathbf{z}_2, \quad \mathbf{z}_4 = \mathbf{z}_1(a^{-1} a') + \mathbf{z}_2(b^{-1} b'),$$

whence $\qquad \{\mathbf{z}_1, \mathbf{z}_2, \mathbf{z}_3, \mathbf{z}_4\} = (a^{-1} a') (b^{-1} b')^{-1}$

$$= a^{-1} a' b'^{-1} b.$$

Hence, substituting the values found above,

$$\{z_1, z_2, z_3, z_4\}$$
$$= \{(23)^{-1}(21).(21)^{-1}(24).(14)^{-1}(12).(12)^{-1}(13)\}$$
$$= \{(23)^{-1}(24).(14)^{-1}(13)\}.$$

We could use this result, of course, to ascertain the changes in the value of the cross-ratio when the order of the points on the line is changed, but the method given above is simpler.

8. Special cases

When the field K is commutative, the expression for the cross-ratio in terms of the non-homogeneous coordinates

$$X_i = x_i y_i^{-1}$$

of the four points becomes

$$\frac{(X_3 - X_1)(X_4 - X_2)}{(X_4 - X_1)(X_3 - X_2)}.$$

We are especially interested in two cases. If $X_2 = \infty$, the expression above reduces to

$$(X_3 - X_1)(X_4 - X_1)^{-1},$$

and if, and only if, $X_1 = (X_3 + X_4)/2$, then

$$\{z_1, z_2, z_3, z_4\} = -1.$$

We therefore obtain a harmonic range in the case when one point is at infinity, and its conjugate point is the "midpoint" of the other two.

The second special case is when the four points X, $-X$, 1, Y, in order, form a harmonic range. Applying the formula above,

$$\frac{(1-X)(Y+X)}{(Y-X)(1+X)} = -1,$$

which leads immediately to

$$Y = X^2.$$

9. The von Staudt theorem

We make use of these results in proving the following theorem, originally proved by von Staudt:

4. *The one–one maps σ of the real line onto itself which preserve harmonic sets must be of the form*

$$\sigma(x) = ax + b \quad (a \neq 0).$$

We assume in the first instance merely that the field K attached to the line is commutative and of characteristic $\neq 2$, and suppose that σ is a one–one map of the line onto itself which maps harmonic sets into harmonic sets. Then, in the first instance, σ^{-1} also has this property.

To prove this, let A', B', C', D' be a harmonic set, and A, B, C, D the images of these points under σ^{-1}. If the fourth harmonic point D^* of A, B, C is finite, then A', B', C', $\sigma(D^*)$ are harmonic, and therefore

$$\sigma(D^*) = D' = \sigma(D),$$

so that $D^* = D$, since σ is one–one.

We assume that $\sigma(\infty) = \infty$. If the coordinates of A, B, C are a, b, c respectively, we know that $(a+b)/2$, ∞, a, b form a harmonic set. By hypothesis

$$\sigma\{(a+b)/2\},\ \infty,\ \sigma(a),\ \sigma(b)$$

form a harmonic set, and therefore, by what we have proved above, we must have

$$\sigma\left\{\frac{(a+b)}{2}\right\} = \frac{\sigma(a)+\sigma(b)}{2}.$$

We see at once that this is a trivial relation if $a = b$.

Assume, for the moment, that $\sigma(0) = 0$ and $\sigma(1) = 1$. If we put $b = 0$,

$$\sigma(a/2) = \sigma(a)/2,$$

and if we write $a/2 = x$ and $b/2 = y$, we have

$$\sigma(x+y) = \sigma(x)+\sigma(y)$$

as a consequence of this last result. If we substitute $x-y$ for x, we have

$$\sigma(x-y+y) = \sigma(x-y)+\sigma(y),$$
or $$\sigma(x-y) = \sigma(x)-\sigma(y),$$

from which, for $x = 0$, we obtain

$$\sigma(-y) = -\sigma(y).$$

We saw above, in the second special case of a harmonic range, that the points

$$x,\quad -x,\quad 1,\quad y$$

form a harmonic range if, and only if, $y = x^2$. The points

$$\sigma(x),\quad -\sigma(x),\quad 1,\quad \sigma(x^2)$$

must form a harmonic range, and therefore
$$\sigma(x^2) = [\sigma(x)]^2.$$
We now have
$$\begin{aligned}
\sigma(xy) &= \sigma[\tfrac{1}{2}\{(x+y)^2 - x^2 - y^2\}] \\
&= \tfrac{1}{2}\sigma[(x+y)^2 - x^2 - y^2] \\
&= \tfrac{1}{2}[\sigma(x+y)^2 - \sigma(x^2) - \sigma(y^2)] \\
&= \tfrac{1}{2}[\{\sigma(x+y)\}^2 - \{\sigma(x)\}^2 - \{\sigma(y)\}^2] \\
&= \tfrac{1}{2}[\{\sigma(x) + \sigma(y)\}^2 - \{\sigma(x)\}^2 - \{\sigma(y)\}^2] \\
&= \sigma(x)\,\sigma(y).
\end{aligned}$$

This result, together with
$$\sigma(x+y) = \sigma(x) + \sigma(y),$$
proves that σ *is an automorphism of K* (see Appendix).

If the conditions $\sigma(0) = 0$, $\sigma(1) = 1$ are not satisfied, we consider the one–one onto mapping defined thus:
$$\tau(x) = [\sigma(x) - \sigma(0)]\,[\sigma(1) - \sigma(0)]^{-1}.$$
Then $\tau(0) = 0$, $\tau(1) = 1$, and it is clear that τ preserves harmonic sets. Hence
$$\tau(x) = x^\tau,$$
where τ is an automorphism of K. If we express σ in terms of τ we have
$$\sigma(x) = [\sigma(1) - \sigma(0)]\,x^\tau + \sigma(0),$$
which is of the form
$$\sigma(x) = ax^\tau + b.$$

We therefore have the theorem:

5. *The one–one maps σ of a line onto itself which preserve harmonic ranges are of the form*
$$\sigma(x) = ax^\tau + b,$$
where $a \neq 0$ and τ is an automorphism of the (commutative) field K.

If K is the field of real numbers, we know that K possesses only the identical automorphism (see Appendix). We therefore have the corollary, von Staudt's theorem:

4. *The one–one maps σ of the real line onto itself which preserve harmonic sets must be of the form*
$$\sigma(x) = ax + b,$$
where $a \neq 0$.

10. Fixed points over a skew field

The preceding section on cross-ratios over a skew field naturally underlines the similarities between the theorems proved here and those which hold when K is commutative. When K is commutative, and therefore the Pappus theorem holds, a projective transformation of the points of a line onto itself cannot have more than two fixed points, if it is not the identity. When K is a skew field, the situation is quite different, as we now show.

Let (x, y) be the right-hand homogeneous coordinates of a point on a given line, and consider the projective transformation

$$x' = cx, \quad y' = cy,$$

where $c \neq 0$ is a fixed arbitrary element of K. We see at once that this transformation is one–one, without exception, changes harmonic sets of points on the line into harmonic sets, and, more generally, leaves unchanged the cross-ratios of any quadruple of points on the line.

For (x, y) to be a fixed point, it is necessary and sufficient that there exists an element $c' \neq 0$ in K such that

$$x' = xc', \quad y' = yc'.$$

This leads to

$$cx = xc', \quad cy = yc', \quad x = cxc'^{-1}, \quad y = cyc'^{-1},$$

and therefore

$$xy^{-1} = c(xy^{-1})c^{-1}.$$

Hence the point (x, y) is fixed if, and only if, its non-homogeneous coordinate $z = xy^{-1}$ is commutative with c. Therefore the points

$$z = \infty, 0, 1$$

or

$$(1, 0), \quad (0, 1), \quad (1, 1)$$

are fixed, but also all the points z which belong to the centre of K are fixed. If c does not belong to the centre of K, not all the points of the line are fixed points.

Since we are discussing fixed points, we stress again that not all plane collineations (Ch. V, §15) are central collineations, thus possessing a line of fixed points. Let K be the field of real numbers, and consider the plane collineation

$$x'_0 = x_1, \quad x'_1 = x_2, \quad x'_2 = x_0.$$

13

For a fixed point (x_0, x_1, x_2) we must have:

$$x_0' = kx_0 = x_1, \quad x_1' = kx_1 = x_2, \quad x_2' = kx_2 = x_0 \quad (k \neq 0).$$

Hence none of $x_0, x_1, x_2 = 0$, and

$$k = \frac{x_1}{x_0} = \frac{x_2}{x_1} = \frac{x_0}{x_2},$$

so that $\qquad\qquad k^3 = (x_1 x_2 x_0)/(x_0 x_1 x_2) = 1.$

The only real root of this equation is $k = 1$, and therefore the only fixed point under the collineation is $(1, 1, 1)$.

CHAPTER IX

CONICS

1. Definition of a conic

In our first introductory chapter we mentioned the conic sections, and in Ch. IV, §3, we gave Poncelet's method for solving certain constructions by finding the fixed points of a definite projective transformation between the points of a given line. To find these fixed points we must use the theory of projective ranges on a conic. In this chapter we introduce the fundamental properties of conic sections, making use of the general theory of previous chapters. The theory is an extensive one, but we shall only develop the fundamental theorems here. If the reader is persuaded that the theory is a beautiful one, he may wish to pursue it further in Baker [4] and other books.

We assume the Pappus theorem and its consequences (Ch. IV) and we shall also assume that *the field of the geometry is such that every non-trivial projective correspondence between the points of a line has two fixed points.*

To define a conic, we consider two pencils of lines, in the same plane, of vertices A and C, and we suppose that these pencils are in projective correspondence. We have discussed projective ranges on two distinct lines very fully in preceding chapters (Ch. III, §2). This is the dual concept.

To any line AP of the first pencil there corresponds a unique line CP of the second pencil; conversely, to any line CP there corresponds a unique line AP. The locus of the points of intersection P of corresponding lines of the two pencils is called a *conic*, or *conic section* (see Fig. 103).

By definition, the conic only contains one further point, besides A, on any line through A, and one further point, besides C, on any line through C. Let l be a line which contains neither A nor C. Then the projective pencils, vertices A and C, cut projective ranges on l, and, by our hypothesis above, these ranges have two fixed points, U and V say. Then AU corresponds to CU, and AV corresponds to CV in the projectivity between the pencils. Hence U and V are points on the conic.

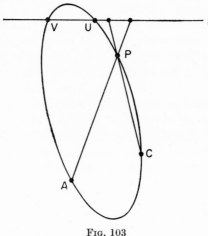

FIG. 103

A line therefore cuts the conic in two points. This remains true if the line l passes through A, say, since there is a line of the pencil vertex A which corresponds to the line CA of the pencil vertex C, and therefore A, and similarly C, both lie on the conic. The line AC cannot cut the conic in points other than A and C.

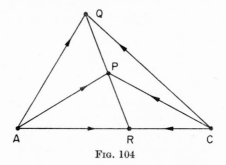

FIG. 104

There is one exceptional case which we now consider. It may happen that to the line AC in the pencil vertex A there corresponds the line CA in the pencil vertex C. When this is so, it is clear that all points of the line AC are, by definition, points of the locus, and we also know (Ch. III, § 19, Lemma 2) that corresponding rays of our two pencils meet in the points of a line. In fact, let P, Q be two points of the locus not on AC, and let PQ meet AC in R. Then the two pencils determine projective ranges on PQ, and P, Q, R are fixed points for these ranges. It follows (Ch. IV, §2) that every point on PQ is a fixed point, that is, every point of PQ is on the locus.

There are no other points besides those on the lines AC and PQ which are on the locus. For if T is such a point, the join of T to any point of PQ gives a line which is part of the locus, and every point of the plane would be on the locus. The complete locus therefore consists of the two lines AC and PQ. Conversely, if the points A and C are chosen on one of two given lines, it is clear that the pencils joining A and C to any point on the other line are projective, and in this correspondence AC corresponds to CA. A pair of lines may therefore be regarded as a (degenerate) conic.

2. Tangent

Having considered this special case, we now suppose that to the ray AC in the pencil vertex A there corresponds a ray CB in the pencil vertex C, where $CB \neq CA$. To the ray CA in the pencil vertex C there will correspond a ray $AB \neq AC$ of the pencil vertex A. We have already noted that the points A and C lie on the locus, being the intersections of the corresponding rays AB and CA, and AC and CB respectively.

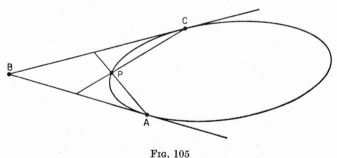

FIG. 105

The line CB is *special* in the sense that the only point in which it meets the conic locus is C. Any other line through $C \neq CB$ will not correspond to the line AC, and will therefore meet the conic in a point $\neq C$. The line CB is called the *tangent* to the conic at C. Similarly the line AB is the *tangent* to the conic at A. We shall soon see that the points A and C can be replaced by any other pair of distinct points on the conic, so that there is a tangent at every point on the conic.

3. Determination by five points

If the lines AB and CB are given as tangents at A and B respectively, and one point P of the locus is also given, then the conic is uniquely determined, since the rays $A(P, C, B)$ and $C(P, B, A)$ must correspond, and the projectivity is therefore uniquely determined.

More generally, if we are given five points, A, C, P_1, P_2, P_3, and suppose that at most one of the P_i lies on AC, then we can draw a conic to pass through the five points. All we have to do is to set up the projectivity in which the rays $A(P_1, P_2, P_3)$ correspond respectively to the rays $C(P_1, P_2, P_3)$. If three of the five points are collinear, the conic is a pair of lines. If four of the points are collinear, there is no unique conic through the five points.

4. Conic as a homogeneous construct

We now show that a conic is a homogeneous construct, in the sense that any two points on it serve equally well as the vertices of projective pencils by which it may be defined.

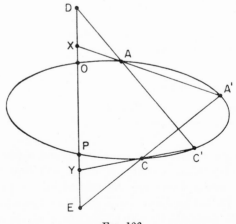

FIG. 106

The points A and C, in Fig. 106, are the vertices of the defining pencils, and we wish to prove that they may be replaced by any two other points, A' and C', say, of the locus.

Let O be any point of the conic, and suppose that any line, drawn through O, meets the conic again in a point P. Let the lines AA' and CC' meet the line OP in X and Y respectively, and let the lines AC' and $A'C$ meet OP in D and E. Then by hypothesis

$$A(A',C',O,P)\,\overline{\wedge}\,C(A',C',O,P),$$

so that

$$(X,D,O,P)\,\overline{\wedge}\,(E,Y,O,P),$$

or

$$(X,D,O,P)\,\overline{\wedge}\,(Y,E,P,O).$$

It follows (Ch. IV, §5, Th. 2) that the three pairs of points (X, Y), (D, E) and (O, P) are in involution.

To prove that pencils vertices A' and C' may be used in defining the conic, we note that

$$A'(X,E,O,P)\,\overline{\wedge}\,C'(X,E,O,P)$$

$$\overline{\wedge}\,C'(Y,D,P,O)$$

$$\overline{\wedge}\,C'(D,Y,O,P),$$

so that

$$A'(A,C,O,P)\,\overline{\wedge}\,C'(A,C,O,P).$$

This proves the theorem, and establishes the fact that there is a tangent at every point of the conic.

We have also proved the theorem:

1. *The conics which pass through four points cut a fixed line in pairs of points in involution.*

5. Conics through four points

Since a conic can be drawn through five points, an infinite number of conics can be drawn through four points. Consider the points A, C, A', C' in the figure above. We saw that a conic through these four points cuts the line DE in the points O and P which are a pair in the involution which contains X and Y and D and E as pairs. Since an involution is uniquely determined by two pairs of points (Ch. IV, §5, Th. 2, Corollary), and since the four points A, C, A', C' determine the pairs (X, Y) and (D, E), the conic through the four points cuts the line DE in point-pairs of a definite involution.

If the lines AC and $A'C'$ cut DE in the points F and G, then (F, G) is also a pair in the involution. We may regard the three line-pairs which contain the points A, C, A', C' as three degenerate conics of the system of conics which passes through the four points.

The theorem just proved has many important consequences, but we move on to derive a method for generating conics which was devised by Maclaurin. This was mentioned in our introductory chapter (Ch. I, §9, Th. 3).

Exercise

1. A given conic passes through two given points A and B. A variable conic through the given points A, B, C and D cuts the given conic in P and Q. Prove that the line PQ passes through a fixed point.

6. Maclaurin's construction of a conic

We have seen that a projectivity between two ranges on distinct lines may be set up by means of two perspectivities (Ch. III, §4, Th. 2). If the lines are a and c, this means that the ranges are both

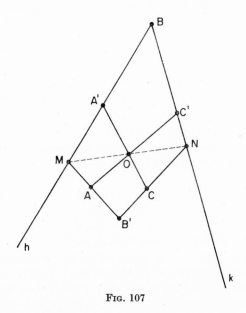

Fig. 107

in perspective with another range, on a line o say, from vertices H and K respectively. The dual result, which we now wish to use, is the following:

Two projective pencils with distinct vertices A and C can always be constructed by joining A and C respectively to the corresponding points M and N of ranges on two distinct lines h and k, where M and N are in perspective from a point O.

Hence the definition of a conic as the locus of the intersection of corresponding rays of two projective pencils is equivalent to the following construction (see Fig. 107):

A variable triangle MNB' moves so that the vertices M and N move on two fixed lines h and k respectively, and the sides MN, NB' and $B'M$ pass through the respective fixed non-collinear points O, C and A. Then the vertex B' describes a conic.

This is Maclaurin's construction, and it was described in Ch. I, §9, Theorem 3.

Conversely, it is clear that the ranges (M) and (N) are projective, being perspective from O. Hence the pencils $A(M)$ and $C(N)$ are projective, so we are back to our former construction.

Exercise

1. If O, C, A are collinear, show that B' describes a line through the intersection of h and k.

7. Pascal's theorem from the construction

We see in the Maclaurin construction that certain points lie on the conic. We know already that A and C are on the conic. Let OC meet h in A', and let OA meet k in C'. Then A' and C' are on the conic. We see that C' is on the locus by taking N at C', and we see that A' is on the locus by taking M at A'.

If B is the intersection of h and k, then when $M = N = B$, the lines CN and AM intersect at B, so that B is also on the conic.

Since the conic contains the five points B, A, C, A', C', we now have a construction, using lines only, for determining any number of points on a conic which passes through five given points. We saw that five points which are not in special position determine a conic, and we can construct the conic by the method given above.

To recapitulate, given five points B, A, C, A', C', we call BA' the line h, and BC' the line k, we let $O = A'C \cap AC'$, we set up a perspective between points M on h and points N on k with centre O, and the points $B' = AM \cap CN$ describe the conic.

It follows that if we have six points A, B, C, A', B', C' of a conic, the three cross-intersections

$$BC' \cap B'C, \quad CA' \cap C'A, \quad AB' \cap A'B,$$

which give the points N, O, M in the figure, are always in line. This is Pascal's theorem:

2. *If A, B, C, A', B', C' are six points on a conic, the intersections of opposite sides of the inscribed hexagon $AC'BA'CB'$,*

$$BC' \cap B'C, \quad CA' \cap C'A, \quad AB' \cap A'B$$

are collinear.

Another proof of this fundamental theorem will be given later.

Exercises

1. Prove the converse of Theorem 2, that if A, B, C, A', B', C' are six points, and the three points $BC' \cap B'C$, $CA' \cap C'A$ and $AB' \cap A'B$ are collinear, then A, B, C, A', B', C' lie on a conic (which may be degenerate).†

2. If ABC and DEF are two coplanar triangles in triple perspective (see Ch. II, § 7), then the six vertices lie on a conic if, and only if, the three centres of perspective are collinear.

3. Consider the various specializations of Pascal's theorem which arise when there is coincidence between pairs of points of the vertices of the inscribed hexagon.

It can be seen that, corresponding to the arrangements of six given points, there are sixty Pascal lines associated with a given hexagon inscribed in a conic. The configuration formed by these lines has been the object of much detailed investigation (see Baker [4]).

The Maclaurin construction gives the tangents to the conic at A and C. The tangent at C corresponds to the ray AC in the pencil vertex A. If AC intersects h in M^* and k in N^*, then if OM^* cuts k in N', the tangent at C is CN', and if ON^* cuts h in M', the tangent at A is AM'.

8. Projective ranges on a conic

To find where the conic cuts a given line l, we must be able to find the fixed points of two projective ranges on l. This is the problem we were confronted with in our discussion of Poncelet's method of false positions (Ch. IV, § 3). There the problem of constructing a quadrilateral whose vertices lie on four given lines and whose sides respectively pass through four given points was seen to be solvable if the fixed points of two projective ranges on a line can be found. We now show how the theory of the conic sections enables us to solve this problem.

We first show that there is a theory of projective ranges on a conic precisely like that of projective ranges on a line. In fact, if A, B,

---

† If the proof considers all the possibilities which may arise, it is bound to be rather long.

C, D are four points on a conic, and X, Y any two other distinct points on the conic, then

$$X(A,B,C,D) \barwedge Y(A,B,C,D).$$

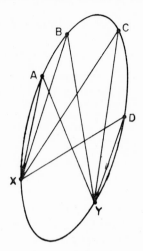

Fig. 108

If we keep the five points A, B, C, D, X fixed, then the point Y is on the conic if, and only if, this projective relation is fulfilled.

If A', B', C', D' is any other set of four points on the conic, we may say that

$$(A,B,C,D) \barwedge (A',B',C',D')$$

if the pencils $X(A,B,C,D)$ and $X(A',B',C',D')$ are projective,

$$X(A,B,C,D) \barwedge X(A',B',C',D')$$

for any one point X on the conic. If this relation be satisfied for any one point X, it is satisfied for all points X, and we also have

$$X(A,B,C,D) \barwedge Y(A',B',C',D')$$

for any X and Y on the conic, since the relation of being projective is a transitive relation.

9. The cross-axis of a correspondence

We may now deal with ranges on a conic, using the theory for ranges on a line. If A, B, C and A', B', C' be given triads of points on a conic, we can determine, given any point D, the point D' of the curve such that

$$(A, B, C, D) \barwedge (A', B', C', D').$$

The Pascal line of a hexagon inscribed in a conic enables us to determine D' with ease. We have the theorem:

3. *If* $(A, B, C, ..., P, Q, ...) \barwedge (A', B', C', ..., P', Q', ...)$ *on a given conic, then all intersections of cross-joins such as* $PQ' \cap P'Q$ *lie on a line.*

We have, by the theory of projective ranges on a conic:

$$P(A', B', C', ..., P', Q', ...) \barwedge P'(A, B, C, ..., P, Q, ...).$$

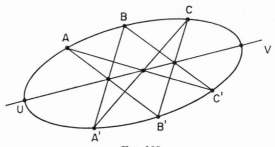

Fig. 109

In these two projective pencils, vertices P and P', the line PP' in the one pencil corresponds to the line $P'P$ in the other pencil. Hence, as we saw above, the intersections of corresponding rays lie on a line, and all intersections of the form $PQ' \cap P'Q$, where P and P' are fixed, lie on this line. If U and V are the fixed points of the projective correspondence, which we suppose to be distinct, then since

$$(A, B, C, ..., U, V, ...) \barwedge (A', B', C', ..., U, V, ...),$$

the points $PU \cap P'U = U$ and $PV \cap P'V = V$ also lie on the line. Since the line UV is determinate, it follows that *all* cross-joins $PQ' \cap P'Q$, for all P, Q and the corresponding P', Q', lie on one line. This line, which may be called *the cross-axis of the correspondence*, meets the conic in the fixed points of the correspondence.

10. Determination of fixed points

A projective correspondence is uniquely defined by the mapping

$$(A, B, C) \barwedge (A', B', C').$$

The cross-axis of the correspondence is given as the Pascal line of the hexagon $AB'CA'BC'$ and, given D, we determine D' by making

$AD' \cap A'D$ lie on the Pascal line. The Pascal line also meets the conic in the fixed points of the projective correspondence we are considering. We therefore have the following simple construction for the fixed points of two projective ranges on a line:

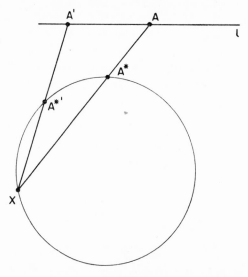

FIG. 110

Take any given conic (a circle is the simplest) and from a given point X on the conic project the points on l into points on the conic, the line joining X to a point P of l intersecting the conic again in a point P^*. With this mapping of points on l onto points on the conic we see at once that if, on the line,

$$(A, B, C, \ldots) \overline{\wedge} (A', B', C', \ldots)$$

then certainly $X(A, B, C, \ldots) \overline{\wedge} X(A', B', C', \ldots)$,

and thus $X(A^*, B^*, C^*, \ldots) \overline{\wedge} X(A^{*'}, B^{*'}, C^{*'}, \ldots)$

and so $(A^*, B^*, C^*, \ldots) \overline{\wedge} (A^{*'}, B^{*'}, C^{*'}, \ldots)$

on the conic.

Conversely we can project from the given point X on the conic back onto the line. If U, V are the fixed points of the projective correspondence on the line, projection from X produces fixed points U^*, V^* of the correspondence on the conic. If we can find U^*, V^* on the conic, projection from X will give us the fixed points U, V

14

of the correspondence on the line in which A, B, C are mapped, respectively, on A', B', C'.

But we can use the Pascal line of the hexagon $A*B*'C*A*'B*C*'$ to determine the fixed points $U*$, $V*$ on the conic. Having carried out this simple construction, projection from X onto the line gives us the fixed points we seek.

The Poncelet problem can therefore be solved, and only three "false" positions need be taken before a solution is possible.

Exercise

1. In Ch. IV, § 3, Ex. 1, carry out the construction to determine the initial path of the ray.

11. Involution ranges on a conic

The theory of involution is a special part of the theory of projective ranges, and is especially simple for involution ranges on a conic. We have the theorem:

4. *A necessary and sufficient condition that the three pairs of points (P, P'), (Q, Q') and (R, R') on a conic should be in involution is that the lines PP', QQ' and RR' should meet in a point.*

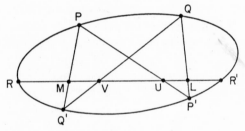

Fig. 111

Let the line RR' meet PP' in U and QQ' in V, and let

$$RR' \cap P'Q = L \quad \text{and} \quad RR' \cap PQ' = M.$$

Since conics through four points cut a line in pairs of points in involution, the pairs (R, R'), (U, V) and (L, M) are in involution. The necessary and sufficient condition for the pairs (P, P'), (Q, Q') and (R, R') on the conic to be in involution is:

$$P(P', Q', R, R') \barwedge P'(P, Q, R', R).$$

Taking sections with the line RR', this is so if, and only if,

$$(U, M, R, R') \barwedge (U, L, R', R).$$

Since the pairs (R, R'), (U, V) and (L, M) are in involution,

$$(U, L, R', R) \barwedge (V, M, R, R'),$$

so that the pairs (P, P'), (Q, Q') and (R, R') are in involution if, and only if,

$$(U, M, R, R') \barwedge (V, M, R, R'),$$

from which we deduce that $U = V$, and the three lines PP', QQ' and RR' are concurrent.

Exercises

1. By representing the involutions on a given line on a given conic, and using the theorem above and Pascal's theorem, prove Theorem 7 of Ch. IV, § 7, that if M, N is a pair of each of the involutions $(PP'')(QQ'')$ and $(P'P'')(Q'Q'')$, then it is also a pair of the involution $(PQ')(QP')$.

2. P, Q, R are three distinct points in the plane of a conic which do not lie on it. Show that there are, in general, two triangles XYZ inscribed in the conic whose sides YZ, ZX and XY pass respectively through P, Q and R. When is there an infinity of such triangles?

12. Pole and polar

We can apply this theory immediately to prove that through any point O of the plane, not lying on a given conic, there pass two tangents of the conic. We saw previously that a line of the plane which is not a tangent meets the conic in two points. We wish to show that through O there pass two lines which only meet the conic in one point.

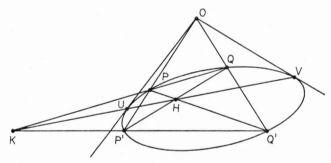

Fig. 112

Let lines be drawn through O meeting the conic in the pairs of points (P, P'), (Q, Q'), (R, R'), ... We have seen that these pairs of points are in involution on the conic. Let U and V be the fixed points of this involution. Then the lines OU and OV only meet the conic in U and V. We can say that U and V are *coincident* points, each counting as two points, since a line which is not a tangent meets the conic in two points. Besides OU and OV, there are no other tangents to the conic through O.

The ranges $(P, Q, R, \dots)$ and $(P', Q', R', \dots)$ being in involution are projective, and the cross-axis is the line joining the fixed points, UV. The lines PQ' and $P'Q$ meet on UV, say in H. But the ranges $(P', Q, R, \dots)$ and $(P, Q', R', \dots)$ belong to the same projectivity, so that $P'Q'$ and PQ also intersect on the line UV, say at K. We can therefore construct the line UV by drawing the line HK when the four points P, P', Q, Q' are given. We deduce that the line PP' cuts UV in a point which is the harmonic conjugate of O with respect to P and P'. Similarly the line QQ' is cut by UV in a point which is the harmonic conjugate of O with respect to Q and Q', and a similar remark is true for every line ORR' which can be drawn through O.

We have therefore proved that if lines be drawn through a point O which is not on the conic, and upon each line the harmonic conjugate of O is taken with respect to the two points in which the line meets the conic, then the locus of this harmonic conjugate is a line, called the *polar line* or *polar* of O with respect to the conic.

It follows immediately from the definition that if the polar of O passes through a point O', then the polar of O' passes through O. For the line OO' cuts the conic in two points such that O and O' are harmonic conjugates with respect to these two points. The points O, O' are then said to be *conjugate* points.

Hence if the line which is the polar of O is given, we can determine O by finding the polars of any two points of the line. These will intersect in O. The point O is called the *pole* of the line which is the polar of O, and each is uniquely determined by the other. If a line l contains the pole of a line m, then m contains the pole of l. Two such lines are said to be *conjugate* lines.

When O is on the conic, our construction for harmonic conjugates must be applied to the case when $O = P \neq P'$, and we seek to determine the harmonic conjugate of O with respect to P and P'. The construction (Ch. III, § 8) is still valid, and shows that $O' = O$. The locus of O does not exist, but we formally define the polar of O to be the tangent to the conic at O. If X is any point on the tangent at O, the polar of X passes through O, and therefore we may still say that if the polar of O passes through X, the polar of X passes through O.

We have defined the polar of O when O is on the conic to be the tangent at O, and the polar of O then passes through O. Conversely, what may we deduce from the fact that the polar of a given point O contains O? If O is not on the conic, there is a line through O which cuts the conic in distinct points P, P', neither of which coincides with O, and the harmonic conjugate of O with respect to P and P' must coincide with O. If we are not in the special case (Ch. III, §12, Th. 9) when the characteristic of the field of the geometry is 2 (Ch. VIII, §6, Th. 3), this is impossible. (We have tacitly assumed, since we wish to talk of harmonic conjugates in a meaningful way, that the field of the geometry is not of characteristic 2.) We therefore deduce that O must lie on the conic. Hence the polar of O contains O if, and only if, O lies on the conic.

Exercises

1. If A' is the pole of BC, B' the pole of CA and C' the pole of AB with respect to a conic S, prove that the triangles ABC, $A'B'C'$ are in perspective.

2. Deduce from the preceding exercise that if two pairs of opposite sides of a given quadrangle are each conjugate lines with respect to a given conic, then so is the third pair.

13. Model for principle of duality

The relation of pole and polar developed above with respect to a given conic S enables us to set up a particular model for the Principle of Duality discussed in an earlier chapter (Ch. I, §7). We associate with a point P its polar p with respect to S. We may think, at first, of P and p as being in distinct superimposed planes. As P moves on a given line PQ, p describes the pencil with vertex $p \cap q$. But since, if $p \cap q$ is regarded as being in the first plane, its polar is PQ in the second plane, we see that the correspondence we have set up is a special one, the line which arises from a given point being the same, whether the point is regarded as lying in one or in the other of the two superimposed planes. The necessary and sufficient conditions for a line to contain the point to which it corresponds is that the point be on the conic S, when the corresponding line will be the tangent to S at the point. The conic may therefore be regarded as the *incidence locus* of the mapping.

If we apply the mapping we have been discussing to the Maclaurin generation of the conic S (§6), we obtain Fig. 113 which shows us that if a and c are fixed tangents to S, then the variable tangent b' cuts projective ranges on these tangents. We also see that if

$ab'ca'bc'$ is a hexagon of tangents to S, then the three lines joining opposite pairs of vertices

$$(a \cap b', a' \cap b), \quad (b \cap c', b' \cap c), \quad (c \cap a', c' \cap a)$$

pass through a point. This theorem, the dual of Pascal's theorem, was discovered by Brianchon, and is known as *Brianchon's theorem*.

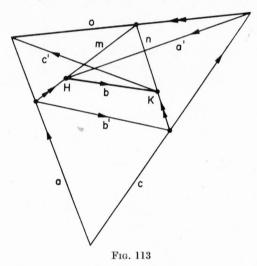

Fig. 113

14. Ranges cut by variable tangent

We end this chapter by proving a stronger result for the ranges cut by a variable tangent to S on fixed tangents. Let the given tangents at the points A and C on S meet in B, and let the variable tangent at P cut BA in T and BC in U. Let AP meet BC in Q, and let AC meet TU in L (see Fig. 114).

The polar of B is AC and contains L. The polar of L therefore contains B, and also P, and is therefore BP. If $BP \cap AC = L'$, the range $\{AC, LL'\}$ is therefore harmonic. If we project this range from P onto BC, we see that B, U are harmonic conjugates of C and Q.

The points C, B are given, and it is easy to show, from first principles, that $(Q) \overline{\wedge} (U)$ (see Ch. III, § 10, Ex. 1).

Now the range (Q) is projective with the range (P) on the conic, being projected from the given point A on the conic. Hence

$$(U) \overline{\wedge} (P) \overline{\wedge} (T),$$

and we have therefore proved that the tangent at a variable point P on the conic cuts given tangents in ranges which are projective with the range of points P on the conic.

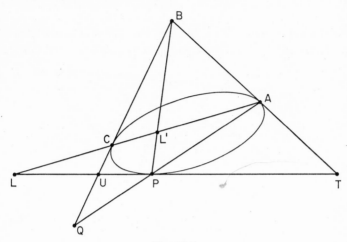

Fig. 114

The dual nature of the conic has now been made clear, and dual theorems for all those proved already are easily written down. But it is not our intention here to pursue the manifold applications of the fundamental theorems. For the rich diversity of such applications we refer the reader to Baker [**4**].

Exercises

1. Examine the special case of Brianchon's theorem when two sides of the hexagon escribed to a conic Σ coincide.

2. $ABCD$ is a parallelogram escribed to a conic Σ which touches CD at F. If H is on BC and E on AB such that FH is parallel to DE, prove that EH touches Σ.

3. If two triangles are inscribed in a conic S, prove that their six sides touch a conic Σ.

4. BC is the chord of contact of tangents from A to a conic S, and EF is the chord of contact of tangents from D. Prove that the sides of the two triangles ABC, DEF touch a conic Σ.

15. From a metrical to a projective view

Since our introductory chapter discussed the different types of conic which arise in the real plane, the ellipse, the parabola and the hyperbola, a word must be said about how these arise in the general theory.

One of the remarkable discoveries of Poncelet in the early part of the nineteenth century was that the properties of conics which appear to be inherently metrical can be regarded as relations of a conic to the line at infinity, and to two special points on that line, the circular points at infinity. If the field of our geometry is that of the real numbers, and points on the line at infinity are associated with directions, or pencils of parallel lines, the circular points are conjugate complex points given by the directions satisfying the equation $m^2 + 1 = 0$. Circles in the real plane, which are defined metrically, are seen to be real conics which pass through the circular points at infinity. Perpendicular lines are lines which cut harmonic conjugates to the circular points on the line at infinity. The midpoint of a segment AB is the harmonic conjugate C' of the point C in which AB meets the line at infinity. The focus of a conic is a point such that the tangents to the conic from the focus pass through the circular points. The corresponding directrix is the polar of the focus. The centre of a conic is the pole of the line at infinity.

From this point of view an ellipse is a real conic which does not cut the line at infinity, a parabola is a real conic which touches the line at infinity, and a hyperbola is a real conic which cuts the line at infinity in two points. The perspective transformations given in Ch. I, § 14, which correspond to the conical projections of a circle which has varying relations to a line projecting into the line at infinity, demonstrate the different types of real conic from this point of view.

More generally we can demonstrate the properties of conics with respect to two fixed points I and J, a circle being defined to be a conic through I and J, its centre as the pole of the line IJ, and we can then prove all the usual results on circles. We absorb the metrical notions already mentioned, defining two lines to be perpendicular if they cut IJ in a pair of points forming a harmonic range with the pair I and J, and so on. A large number of theorems, usually regarded as metrical, can be proved, with these definitions, from projective considerations. This can be seen in Baker [4]. The theory can be extended even further, the two points I and J being replaced by a line conic, but we shall not pursue the matter here.

Exercise

1. V is a given point on a conic S, and the points P, Q on the conic are such that VP is perpendicular to VQ. Prove that P, Q are in involution on S, and deduce that the chord PQ passes through a fixed point on the normal to the conic at V.

CHAPTER X

PROJECTIVE SPACE OF n DIMENSIONS

1. Linear spaces

We give here a brief account of the incidence properties of projective space of n dimensions. This can be approached in two ways. We could assume that the projective space is defined over a skew field K. The treatment is then based on the theory of vector spaces over the field K. (For a full account see Hodge and Pedoe [**11**].) Or we may adopt the more abstract view, also given in the work cited above, and begin by postulating the existence of certain objects, each of which has a dimension number attached to it, which may be 0, 1, 2, ...

We call the zero-dimensional objects *points*, the one-dimensional objects *lines*, the two-dimensional *planes*, and so on, and we also postulate a binary relation which may exist between these objects, which we call *linear spaces*.

If this relation holds between a linear space of p dimensions, denoted by S_p, and a linear space of q dimensions, S_q, we say that S_p *lies in* S_q, and write

$$S_p \subseteq S_q.$$

This relation is also written

$$S_q \supseteq S_p,$$

and is then translated as "S_q contains S_p".

2. Axioms

We require this relation to effect a *partial ordering* of our set of linear spaces, and we therefore adopt the following axioms:

    I. For all S_p, $S_p \subseteq S_p$.

    II. If $S_p \subseteq S_q$ and $S_q \subseteq S_p$, then $S_p = S_q$.

    III. If $S_p \subseteq S_q$ and $S_q \subseteq S_r$, then $S_p \subseteq S_r$.

We now introduce a new term. We say that the $p+1$ points $P_0, P_1, ..., P_p$ are *linearly dependent* if there is a linear space S_q of q dimensions containing them, where $q < p$. That is

$$P_i \subseteq S_q \quad (i = 0, 1, ..., p).$$

Points which are not linearly dependent are said to be *linearly independent*.

The following additional axioms characterize the incidence properties of projective space of n dimensions:

IV. Every line contains at least three distinct points.

V. Given any $p+1$ linearly independent points, there is at least one linear space of p dimensions which contains them.

VI. Any linear space of p dimensions contains at least one set of $p+1$ linearly independent points.

VII. If $P_0, ..., P_p$ are $p+1$ linearly independent points which lie in an S_q, any S_p containing them is contained in S_q.

VIII. If $P_0, ..., P_p$ are $p+1$ linearly independent points of an S_p, and $Q_0, ..., Q_q$ are $q+1$ linearly independent points of an S_q, and if the $p+q+2$ points $P_0, ..., P_p$, $Q_0, ..., Q_q$ are linearly dependent, there exists at least one point R which lies in both S_p and S_q.

IX. There exists an integer $n \geqslant 1$ such that there is at least one set of $n+1$ linearly independent points, but any set of m points, where $m > n+1$, is linearly dependent.

These postulates are known to be consistent, since they are satisfied by a projective space of n dimensions defined over a skew field.

3. Deductions

They are not independent. In fact we can deduce Axiom I immediately from VI and VII. For by VI, S_p contains $p+1$ linearly independent points. By VII, any S'_p containing these points lies in S_p. Choose $S'_p = S_p$, and $S_p \subseteq S_p$.

But we are not aiming at a minimal set of axioms. We now prove:

(1) If $S_p \subseteq S_q$, then $p \leqslant q$.

By VI, there is a set of $p+1$ linearly independent points lying in S_p. By III, these lie in S_q. If $q < p$, these points would be linearly dependent. Hence $p \leqslant q$.

(2) If $S_p \subseteq S'_p$, then $S_p = S'_p$.

By III, if $P_0, ..., P_p$ are $p+1$ linearly independent points of S_p, then they are $p+1$ linearly independent points of S'_p. Hence, by VII, $S'_p \subseteq S_p$, and so, by II, $S_p = S'_p$.

(3) The S_p containing $p+1$ linearly independent points is therefore unique, and any set of $p+1$ independent points of an S_p serves to determine it.

We call any set of $p+1$ linearly independent points in an S_p a *basis* for the S_p.

We prove:

(4) Any subset of a linearly independent set of points is necessarily a linearly independent set.

Let $P_0, \ldots, P_p$ be $p+1$ independent points, and suppose that $P_0, \ldots, P_s$ is a linearly dependent subset. Then $P_0, \ldots, P_s$ lie in some S_t, where $t < s$. Let $Q_0, \ldots, Q_t$ be a basis for S_t, and consider the $q+1 = p-s+t+1$ points $Q_0, \ldots, Q_t, P_{s+1}, \ldots, P_p$. If these are linearly independent they determine an S_q. In any case, they lie in an S_r, where $r \leqslant q < p$. Now, S_r contains $Q_0, \ldots, Q_t$ and therefore, by VII, S_t. Hence, by III, S_r contains $P_0, \ldots, P_s$. Again, S_r contains $P_{s+1}, \ldots, P_p$. Hence $P_0, \ldots, P_s, P_{s+1}, \ldots, P_p$ are contained in S_r $(r < p)$, and are therefore linearly dependent. From this contradiction it follows that $P_0, \ldots, P_s$ cannot be linearly dependent.

4. Intersection of two spaces

(5) The points common to an S_p and an S_q are all the points of a linear space.

Let $P_0, \ldots, P_p$ be a basis for S_p, and let $Q_0, \ldots, Q_q$ be a basis for S_q. If S_p and S_q have no common point, it follows from VIII that $P_0, \ldots, P_p, Q_0, \ldots, Q_q$ are linearly independent.

Suppose that S_p and S_q have at least one point in common. Considering the set of common points, there exists an integer r $(0 \leqslant r \leqslant n)$ such that there is at least one set $A_0, \ldots, A_r$ of $r+1$ linearly independent points common to S_p and S_q, but any set of m points $(m > r+1)$ common to S_p and S_q must be linearly dependent.

Now $A_0, \ldots, A_r$ determine an S_r. Since $A_i \subseteq S_p$ $(i = 0, \ldots, r)$, it follows from VII that $S_r \subseteq S_p$. Similarly $S_r \subseteq S_q$. Hence, by (1), $r \leqslant \min(p, q)$. Also, if the point R lies in S_r, then $R \subseteq S_r \subseteq S_p$, and therefore, by III, $R \subseteq S_p$. Similarly, $R \subseteq S_q$. On the other hand, if the point B lies in S_p and in S_q, the points $A_0, \ldots, A_r, B$ are linearly dependent, and therefore lie in an S_t $(t \leqslant r)$. Since $A_i \subseteq S_t$ $(i = 0, \ldots, r)$, $S_r \subseteq S_t$, and therefore $r \leqslant t$. It follows that $r = t$, and, by (2), $S_r = S_t$. Hence the points common to S_p and S_q are all the points of a linear space S_r.

If S_l is any space lying both in S_p and in S_q, and $C_0, \ldots, C_l$ is a basis for S_l, then the points of this basis lie in S_p and S_q, and therefore in S_r. Hence, by VII, S_l lies in S_r.

(6) If S_p and S_q have at least one point in common, the $p+q+2$ points $P_0, ..., P_p$, $Q_0, ..., Q_q$ (with the notation of (5)) are linearly dependent.

This is the converse of VIII. As above, let S_r be the linear space containing all the points common to S_p and S_q. If $p>r$, there exists a point in S_p which is not in S_r. Otherwise $S_p \subseteq S_r$, and hence $p \leqslant r$. Let B_{r+1} be a point which is in S_p, but not in S_r. Then $A_0, ..., A_r$, B_{r+1} must be linearly independent, where $A_0, ..., A_r$ are a basis for S_r. Otherwise we could show, as above, that $B_{r+1} \subseteq S_r$. Hence $A_0, ..., A_r$, B_{r+1} determine an $S_{r+1} \subseteq S_p$. If $p>r+1$, we can similarly find another point in S_p, B_{r+2}, say, such that $A_0, ..., A_r$, B_{r+1}, B_{r+2} are linearly independent.

If we continue in this way, we obtain a basis $A_0, ..., A_r$, $B_{r+1}, ..., B_p$ for S_p whose first $r+1$ points are a basis for S_r. In the same way we can construct a basis $A_0, ..., A_r$, $C_{r+1}, ..., C_q$ for S_q. If the points $A_0, ..., A_r$, $B_{r+1}, ..., B_p$, $C_{r+1}, ..., C_q$ are linearly independent, they determine a linear space of $p+q-r$ dimensions. In any case, they determine an S_t ($t \leqslant p+q-r$).

Since S_t contains $A_0, ..., A_r$, $B_{r+1}, ..., B_p$, it contains S_p, and therefore, by III, $P_0, ..., P_p$. Similarly, it contains S_q, and therefore $Q_0, ..., Q_q$. Hence the set $P_0, ..., P_p$, $Q_0, ..., Q_q$ lies in S_t, where

$$t \leqslant p+q-r < p+q+1,$$

and is therefore linearly dependent.

5. Join of two spaces

(7) The set of points $A_0, ..., A_r$, $B_{r+1}, ..., B_p$, $C_{r+1}, ..., C_q$ is a linearly independent set.

Let us suppose the points are linearly dependent. The points $A_0, ..., A_r$, $B_{r+1}, ..., B_p$ are independent, by construction, and determine S_p. The set $C_{r+1}, ..., C_q$ is a subset of a linearly independent set, and therefore, by (4) above, is linearly independent, and determines an S_{q-r-1}. If our hypothesis is correct, and $A_0, ..., A_r$, $B_{r+1}, ..., B_p$, $C_{r+1}, ..., C_q$ are dependent, then, by VIII, S_p and S_{q-r-1} have a point, R say, in common.

Since $C_i \subseteq S_q$ ($i = r+1, ..., q$), it follows that $S_{q-r-1} \subseteq S_q$, and therefore R lies in S_q. It also lies in S_p, and therefore, by (5), R lies in S_r.

Therefore S_r and S_{q-r-1} have the point R in common, and by (6) above it follows that $A_0, ..., A_r$, $C_{r+1}, ..., C_q$ must be linearly dependent. This contradiction proves that $A_0, ..., A_r, B_{r+1}, ..., B_p,$ $C_{r+1}, ..., C_q$ are linearly independent.

These points therefore determine an S_{p+q-r}. This result still holds if S_p and S_q have no point in common, provided we put $r = -1$.

Now, $S_p \subseteq S_{p+q-r}$ and $S_q \subseteq S_{p+q-r}$. On the other hand, if S_k is any linear space such that $S_p \subseteq S_k$ and also $S_q \subseteq S_k$, then $A_0, ..., A_r,$ $B_{r+1}, ..., B_p, C_{r+1}, ..., C_q$ are all in S_k, so that $S_{p+q-r} \subseteq S_k$.

Hence S_{p+q-r} is contained in every linear space which contains both S_p and S_q. We call this space the *join* of S_p and S_q, and the space S_r is called the *intersection* of S_p and S_q. We write

$$S_{p+q-r} = S_p + S_q, \quad S_r = S_p \cap S_q,$$

and we have proved

1. *The dimension r of the intersection of two linear spaces S_p and S_q is connected with the dimension t of their join by the relation*

$$r + t = p + q.$$

6. The complementation theorem

We now show that any given S_p in our projective space of n dimensions, S_n, can be complemented by a space S_{n-p-1} which is such that S_p and S_{n-p-1} have no intersection, and their join is S_n.

Let the given space S_p have a basis consisting of the points $P_0, ..., P_p$. We assume that $p < n$. By IX above, there is a set of $n+1$ linearly independent points, $Q_0, ..., Q_n$, say. This set cannot all lie in S_p, since they are independent, so that at least one point of the set, which we may call Q_0, does not lie in S_p.

The set $P_0, ..., P_p, Q_0$ cannot be linearly dependent, since if it were, the points would lie, at worst, in an S_p', and by (3) above there is only one S_p containing $P_0, ..., P_p$, and it does not contain Q_0. Hence $P_0, ..., P_p, Q_0$ determine an S_{p+1}.

If $p + 1 < n$, not all the points $Q_1, ..., Q_n$ can lie in S_{p+1}, since the points $Q_0, Q_1, ..., Q_n$ would then lie in S_{p+1} and be linearly dependent. Hence at least one point, say Q_1, does not lie in S_{p+1}. Repeating the argument just given, the points $P_0, ..., P_p, Q_0, Q_1$ are independent, and determine an S_{p+2}.

We continue thus until we have an S_{p+r} determined by $P_0, ..., P_p,$ $Q_0, ..., Q_{r-1}$, where $p + r = n$, and then $S_{p+r} = S_n$, by (3).

The points $Q_0, ..., Q_{r-1}$ are a subset of an independent set, and therefore determine an $S_{r-1} = S_{n-p-1}$. Since the set $P_0, ..., P_p,$ $Q_0, ..., Q_{r-1}$ is independent, (6) shows that S_p and S_{n-p-1} have no points in common. The definition of *join* given in (7) also shows that

$$S_n = S_p + S_{n-p-1}.$$

What we have proved here is the equivalent of the *Exchange Theorem* in algebra. We have replaced $p+1$ points of a basis for S_n by the $p+1$ points of a basis for S_p, the new set of $n+1$ points still forming a basis for S_n.

7. Dedekind's law

We now show that our linear spaces obey *Dedekind's law*:

2. *If R, S, T are linear spaces in S_n, and $R \subseteq S$, then*

$$S \cap (R+T) = R + (S \cap T).$$

If $R = T$, then $R+T = R$, $S \cap (R+T) = S \cap R = R$, and

$$R + (S \cap T) = R + (S \cap R) = R + R = R.$$

We may therefore assume that $R \neq T$.

If $S = R$, we have to prove that $S \cap (S+T) = S + (S \cap T)$. But each side is equal to S.

We may therefore also assume that $S \neq R$.

From our definitions of intersection and join it is clear that $S \cap T \subseteq S$, and since $R \subseteq S$,

$$R + (S \cap T) \subseteq S.$$

Again, since $S \cap T \subseteq T$,

$$R + (S \cap T) \subseteq R + T.$$

Therefore $$R + (S \cap T) \subseteq S \cap (R+T).$$

To prove that

$$S \cap (R+T) \subseteq R + (S \cap T),$$

let s be a point in $S \cap (R+T)$. Since $R \subseteq S$, such a point exists. Since s is in $R+T$, we can find a point r in R and a point t in T such that s, r and t are linearly dependent, that is, collinear. Since $S \neq R$, and $R \neq T$, the points r and t can be chosen to be distinct from s and from each other.

Since $R \subseteq S$, both r and s are in S, and therefore t is linearly dependent on points in S. Hence t lies in S, and also in T, and therefore lies in $S \cap T$. The point s is linearly dependent on r and on t, and therefore lies in $R + (S \cap T)$. Since s is any point in

$S \cap (R+T)$, this proves that

$$S \cap (R+T) \subseteq R + (S \cap T),$$

and therefore that

$$S \cap (R+T) = R + (S \cap T).$$

We have now proved that our linear spaces in S_n, partially ordered with respect to inclusion, form a *complete, complemented, modular lattice*, using terms which will be found in Lattice Theory [**5**].

The greatest lower bound of any set of linear spaces is their common intersection, and the least upper bound is their join. The intersection and join of a set of linear spaces can be defined inductively. Or we can approach these concepts by another path, and note that the intersection of a set of spaces is the join of all linear spaces common to the set, and the join of a set is the intersection of all spaces which contain every linear space of the set.

8. Projection

The notion of *projection*, or *perspectivity*, used in the early chapters extends to projective space of n dimensions. Let R be a given linear space in S_n, and let T and T' be spaces which are both

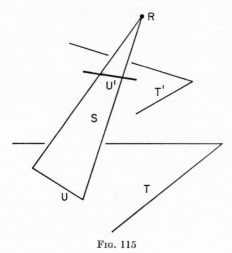

FIG. 115

complementary to R. Then

$$S_n = R + T = R + T',$$
$$0 = R \cap T = R \cap T',$$

where 0 stands for the empty intersection. If $S \supseteq R$, Dedekind's law gives

$$S \cap (R+T) = S \cap S_n = S = R + (S \cap T) = R + U,$$

where we write $U = S \cap T$. This gives

$$S = R + U.$$

For subspaces U of T and spaces $S \supseteq R$, the two relations

$$U = S \cap T \quad \text{and} \quad S = R + U$$

are equivalent.

We now start with any $U \subseteq T$, form $S = U + R$, and intersect S with T', any other complement to R in S_n. Define $U' = S \cap T'$. This gives a one–one correspondence between the subspaces U of T and the subspaces U' of T' which is completely described by the one equation:

$$U + R = U' + R.$$

Since $U_1 \subseteq U_2$, for two U_1, U_2 in T, implies $U'_1 \subseteq U'_2$, this one–one correspondence is a collineation of the projective space T onto the projective space T'. It is called *the projection of T onto T' from the centre R.*

ALGEBRAIC RESULTS QUOTED IN TEXT

It is convenient to list the results used in the text. We shall not endeavour to précis proofs, but refer the reader to Birkhoff and MacLane [6] where most of the theorems we need are proved.

A *group* is a system of elements which is closed under a single-valued binary operation which is associative, and relative to which it contains an element satisfying the identity law, and with each element another element (called its inverse) satisfying the inverse law.

If elements are denoted by $a, b, c, ...$, and the result of the binary operation applied to a and b by ab, the three laws defining groups are:

Associative Law: $a(bc) = (ab)c$ for all a, b, c.

Identity Law: $ae = ea = a$ for all a, where e is the identity element.

Inverse Law: $aa^{-1} = a^{-1}a = e$ for each a and some a^{-1}.

If $ab = ba$ for all a and b, the group is called a *commutative* or *Abelian* group, and the group operation applied to a and b is usually denoted by $a+b$. The identity element is then denoted by 0, so that $a+0 = 0+a = a$ for all a.

In any group the identity e can be shown to be unique. The inverse a^{-1} of any given element a is likewise unique.

A *quasi-group* Q is a system of elements $a, b, c, ...$ in which a binary operation on a and b, denoted by ab, is defined such that in $ab = c$ any two of a, b, c determine the third uniquely as an element of Q.

A *loop* is a quasi-group with an identity element e such that $ea = ae = a$ for every element a.

A *subgroup* of a group G is a subset of the elements which itself forms a group with respect to the binary operation as defined in G.

The identity element of the subgroup is the identity element of G.

If G and H are groups between the elements of which there is a one–one correspondence such that group relations are preserved, then the groups are said to be *isomorphic*.

If $a, b, c, ...$, are mapped on $a', b', c', ...$ then from $ab = c$ we must be able to deduce that $a'b' = c'$, and conversely.

15   207

The identity of G is then mapped on the identity of H.

If the groups G and H are the same group, the mapping $a \to a'$ is called an *automorphism*.

If a is a fixed element of G, the mapping

$$x \to x' = axa^{-1}$$

is an automorphism, since we find x given uniquely in terms of x' by the relation

$$x = a^{-1}x'a,$$

showing that the mapping is one–one, and also

$$x'y' = (axa^{-1})(aya^{-1}) = a(xy)a^{-1} = (xy)',$$

so that the group relation is preserved.

The elements x, axa^{-1} are said to be *conjugate* elements. The automorphisms discussed are called *inner automorphisms*. Any others are called *outer* automorphisms.

The *centre* of a group is the set of elements a which permute with all elements x of the group, so that $ax = xa$. We then have

$$axa^{-1} = x$$

so that an element and its conjugate are the same. In an Abelian group, where all elements belong to the centre, there are no inner automorphisms distinct from the identical automorphism $x \to x$.

If G and H are groups between the elements of which there is a *many*–one correspondence such that group relations are preserved, then G is said to be mapped *homomorphically onto H*.

If $a, b, c, \dots$ are mapped upon $a', b', c', \dots$ then from $ab = c$ we must be able to deduce that $a'b' = c'$. Every element of G is mapped upon some element of H, and every element of H is the map of some element of G. This latter notion is the explanation of the phrase *onto*, which will occur later also.

Under any homomorphism the identity is mapped upon the identity, and inverses are mapped upon inverses.

These notions can be extended to *rings*.

A *ring* A is a system of elements which is an Abelian group under an operation of addition, and which is closed under a binary operation of multiplication, which is associative, and distributive with respect to addition. Thus, for all a, b, c in the ring A,

$a(bc) = (ab)c$, multiplication is associative,

$\left. \begin{aligned} a(b+c) &= ab+ac \\ (a+b)c &= ac+bc \end{aligned} \right\}$, multiplication is distributive.

A ring necessarily has a zero element 0 such that $a+0 = 0+a = a$ for all a, and $a.0 = 0$ on multiplication. But rings need not possess an identity element e such that $ae = ea = a$. The even integers form a ring of this kind.

If a ring contains at least one element distinct from zero, and there is always a solution for the equations

$$ax = b,$$

$$ya = b,$$

for $a \neq 0$, it is called a *field*, or an *associative division ring*, or a *skew field*, the latter term being used when it is desired to emphasize that multiplication is not necessarily commutative.

In a skew field the non-zero elements form a group under multiplication. A skew field unites in itself two groups: the multiplicative and the additive groups. They are connected by the distributive laws.

If R and S are two systems in each of which addition and multiplication are defined, the mapping $a \to a'$, where $a \in R$ and $a' \in S$, is called a *homomorphism* if $a \to a'$ and $b \to b'$ involves

$$a+b \to a'+b' \quad \text{and} \quad ab \to a'b'.$$

If the mapping is not many–one, but one–one, the systems are said to be *isomorphic*, and all algebraic properties are carried over from R to S. We deal with the automorphisms of a special field, the field of real numbers, later.

If R is a ring, its homomorphic image S is also a ring. The zero-element in R is mapped on the zero-element in S; if $a \to a'$ then $-a \to -a'$, and if R has an identity element e, it is mapped on an identity element in S. Again, if R is commutative, so is S.

A many–one mapping $a \to a'$ between sets of elements $a \in R$ and $a' \in S$ divides the elements of R into mutually exclusive subsets. All the elements in a particular subset are mapped on the same element of S.

This relation between elements of R is a particular example of an *equivalence* relation which may hold between elements of a set R. If we denote the relation which may hold between two elements a and b of R by the symbol $\equiv$, it is called an *equivalence relation* if it is:

Reflexive: $a \equiv a$ for all a in R,

Symmetric: $a \equiv b$ implies $b \equiv a$ for all a, b in R,

Transitive: $a \equiv b$ and $b \equiv c$ implies $a \equiv c$ for all a, b, c in R.

If such a relation holds, it can be used to divide R into mutually exclusive subsets, the elements in a particular subset being equivalent to each other.

An important application of this notion is to the ring of ordinary integers. Let p be any fixed prime number. We shall say that the integers r and s are *equivalent modulo* p, written

$$r \equiv s(p),$$

if $r - s$ is an integral multiple of p. This is an equivalence relation, and divides the integers into p mutually exclusive sets. These sets can be labelled $0', 1', 2', ..., (p-1)'$, addition and multiplication between elements in the subsets defined, and we see that the elements $0', 1', ..., (p-1)'$ form *a finite commutative field containing* p *elements*.

In this field

$$1' + 1' + ... \text{ to } p \text{ terms} = 0'.$$

Any given skew field K contains a smallest field, called its *prime field*, and the structure of this field is either that of the finite field we have just discussed or that of the field of the rational numbers.

In the first case we say that the skew field has *characteristic p*. If e is the unity of the field then p is the least positive number such that $pe = 0$.

In the second case, the field is said to have *characteristic 0*.

A *vector space* (often called *linear space*) $\mathbf{V}$ over a field K is a set of elements, called vectors, such that any two vectors $\mathbf{x}$ and $\mathbf{y}$ of V determine a unique vector $\mathbf{x}+\mathbf{y}$ as sum, and any vector $\mathbf{x}$ from $\mathbf{V}$ and any element (or scalar) c from K determine a scalar product $c.\mathbf{x}$ in $\mathbf{V}$ with the properties below, for all $\mathbf{x}$, $\mathbf{y}$ in V, all c, c' in K.

(1) $\mathbf{V}$ is an Abelian group under addition,

(2) $c.(\mathbf{x}+\mathbf{y}) = c.\mathbf{x}+c.\mathbf{y}$,
    $(c+c').\mathbf{x} = c.\mathbf{x}+c'.\mathbf{x}$,

(3) $(cc').\mathbf{x} = c.(c'.\mathbf{x})$,
    $1.\mathbf{x} = \mathbf{x}$.

The vectors $\mathbf{x}_1, ..., \mathbf{x}_n$ are *linearly independent* over K if, and only if, for all scalars c_i in K,

$$c_1.\mathbf{x}_1 + c_2.\mathbf{x}_2 + ... + c_n.\mathbf{x}_n = \mathbf{0}$$

implies $\qquad c_1 = c_2 = ... = c_n = 0.$

If $x_1, \ldots, x_n$ are a linearly independent set of vectors of **V** which are such that any vector **x** of **V** can be expressed in the form

$$x = c_1 . x_1 + c_2 . x_2 + \ldots + c_n . x_n,$$

we say that the vectors $x_1, \ldots, x_n$ form *a basis* for **V**, and that **V** has *dimension n*.

We have met fields with a finite number of elements already, the prime fields of characteristic p. Finite commutative fields are generally known as *Galois fields* after their discoverer Galois.

Let G be a Galois field, and let q be the number of its elements. The characteristic of G cannot be zero; for then the prime field G^* in G would already contain an infinity of elements. Let p be the characteristic. Then G^* is isomorphic to the field of residues modulo p already discussed, and contains p elements.

G can be regarded as *a vector space over G^**, and since it contains only a finite number of elements, there can only be a finite number of linearly independent elements over G^* in any maximal set of such elements of G. If $\alpha_1, \ldots, \alpha_n$ is such a set, then any element of G can be expressed in the form

$$c_1 \alpha_1 + c_2 \alpha_2 + \ldots + c_n \alpha_n,$$

with uniquely determined coefficients c_i in G^*.

For every coefficient c_i there are p possible values. Hence there are exactly p^n expressions of the above form, and it follows that

$$q = p^n.$$

It can be shown that for any given p and n such a Galois field exists, and for given p and n all such fields are isomorphic.

A famous theorem of Wedderburn states that all finite skew fields are necessarily commutative, and must therefore be Galois fields. (See Hall [**9**].)

In a finite field of characteristic p, the mapping $a \to a^p$ is an automorphism of the field. It follows that in such a field every element has a pth root.

Since a proof is not easily accessible, we now prove the theorem used in the text on the automorphisms of the field of real numbers.

We shall show that *the field of real numbers has only the identical automorphism*. An automorphism is a one–one mapping ϕ of the real line onto itself which has the properties:

$$\phi(a+b) = \phi(a) + \phi(b), \quad \phi(ab) = \phi(a) \phi(b).$$

We see at once that

$$\phi(0) = \phi(0+0) = \phi(0)+\phi(0),$$

so that $$\phi(0) = 0,$$

and since $$\phi(1) = \phi(1^2) = [\phi(1)]^2,$$

and $\phi(0) \neq \phi(1)$, since the mapping is one–one,

$$\phi(1) = 1.$$

From $\phi(0) = \phi(a-a) = \phi(a)+\phi(-a)$, it follows that

$$\phi(-a) = -\phi(a),$$

and from $$\phi(1) = \phi(a \cdot a^{-1}) = \phi(a)\,\phi(a^{-1}),$$

that $$\phi(a^{-1}) = [\phi(a)]^{-1} \quad (a \neq 0).$$

To prove our theorem we shall make use of two properties of the real number system:

1. *It is Archimedean ordered.*
2. *If $a > 0$, then $\sqrt{a}$ is in the field.*

From the second property we see at once that if $a > 0$, then $\phi(a) = [\phi(\sqrt{a})]^2 > 0$. Hence, if

$$a-b > 0,$$

$$\phi(a-b) = \phi(a)-\phi(b) > 0.$$

We have, of course, for the natural integers n,

$$\phi(n) = \phi(1+1+\ldots+1) = n\phi(1) = n$$

and $$\phi(na) = \phi(a+a+\ldots+a) = n\phi(a).$$

Condition 1 means that for any two numbers $a > 0$ and $b > 0$ from the field of real numbers there exists an integer m for which $mb > a$. Choose $b = 1$, and let $a > 0$ be any given element of the field, and n any given integer. We can always find an integer m such that $m \cdot 1 = m > na$. Let us determine the minimal value of m, so that

$$m-1 \leqslant na < m.$$

These inequalities, by what we have proved, lead to

$$m-1 \leqslant n\phi(a) < m.$$

We see from these two sets of inequalities that the numbers na and $n\phi(a)$ are both in an interval of length 1, so that their difference is less than 1:

$$-1 < n[a-\phi(a)] < 1.$$

If $a > \phi(a)$, this gives $n < [a - \phi(a)]^{-1}$ for every natural number n. If $a < \phi(a)$, then $n < [\phi(a) - a]^{-1}$, which is also absurd. Therefore

$$\phi(a) = a \quad (a > 0).$$

From $a + (-a) = 0$ we have $\phi(-a) = -\phi(a)$, so that

$$\phi(a) = a \quad (a < 0),$$

and with $$\phi(0) = 0$$

we have proved that ϕ is the identical automorphism.

We conclude this summary of results with the *general* notion of a *transformation* or *mapping* of a non-empty S into a set T. By this we mean a rule ϕ which assigns to each element $p \in S$ a unique image element in T.

This is the usual functional notion, and the image can be represented by $\phi(p)$, or by $p\phi$, or by p^ϕ. We merely have to be consistent. We keep to the $p\phi$ notation here.

The set $S\phi$ of all images under ϕ of elements in S may not comprise the whole of T. When the whole of T is, in fact, covered, so that every $q \in T$ is the image $q = p\phi$ of at least one $p \in S$, we say that ϕ is a transformation or mapping of S *onto* T.

If ϕ carries distinct elements into distinct elements, so that $p\phi = p'\phi$ implies $p = p'$, or, equivalently, so that each $q \in T$ is the image of at most one $p \in S$, then ϕ is a *one–one* mapping from S into T.

We now restrict ourselves to mappings of a set S into itself. The *product* $\phi\psi$ of two mappings is simply defined as

$$p(\phi\psi) = (p\phi)\psi,$$

and obeys the associative law. The *identity* mapping I is defined by

$$pI = p \quad (\text{all } p \in S),$$

and then $$I\phi = \phi I = \phi \quad (\text{all } \phi).$$

If $\phi\psi = I$ then ϕ is called a *left-inverse* of ψ, and ψ a *right-inverse* of ϕ. These concepts are related to those of *one–one* and *onto* defined above. We have the theorem:

A transformation $\phi : S \to S$ is one–one if, and only if, it has a right-inverse. It is onto if, and only if, it has a left-inverse.

In the case we are especially interested in, when ϕ is a one–one mapping of S onto S, any right-inverse of ϕ is equal to any left-inverse, and ϕ simply has a unique inverse ϕ^{-1}. We then say that ϕ is an *invertible* mapping.

This leads to the concept of a *group of transformations* on a space S. By this we mean any set G of *one–one* transformations ϕ of S onto S which are such that (i) the identity transformation of S lies in G; (ii) if ϕ is in G, so is its inverse; (iii) if ϕ and ψ are in G, so is their product $\phi\psi$.

Our final result is that the set G of *all* one–one transformations of any space S onto itself is a group of transformations.

BIBLIOGRAPHY

1. ARTIN, E. *Geometric Algebra* (New York, 1957).
2. BAER, R.
   Nets and groups, *Trans. Amer. Math. Soc.* **46**, 110–141 (1939).
   Homogeneity of projective planes, *Amer. J. Math.* **64**, 137–152 (1942).
   A unified theory of projective spaces and finite Abelian groups, *Trans. Amer. Math. Soc.* **52**, 283–343 (1942).
   The fundamental theorems of elementary geometry, *Trans. Amer. Math. Soc.* **56**, 94–129 (1944).
   Projectivities with fixed points on every line of the plane, *Bull. Amer. Math. Soc.* **52**, 273–286 (1946).
   Polarities in finite projective planes, *Bull. Amer. Math. Soc.* **52**, 77–93 (1946).
   Projectivities of finite projective planes, *Amer. J. Math.* **69**, 653–684 (1947).
3. BAER, R. *Linear Algebra and Projective Geometry* (New York, 1952).
4. BAKER, H. F. *Principles of Geometry* (Vol. II, Cambridge, 1922).
5. BIRKHOFF, G. *Lattice Theory* (New York, 1948).
6. BIRKHOFF, G. and MACLANE, S. *A Survey of Modern Algebra* (New York, 1959).
7. CRONHEIM, A. A proof of Hessenberg's theorem, *Proc. Amer. Math. Soc.* **4**, 219–221 (1953).
8. HALL, M., Jnr.
   Projective planes, *Trans. Amer. Math. Soc.* **54**, 229–277 (1943).
   Cyclic projective planes, *Duke Math. J.* **14**, 1079–1090 (1947).
   Corrections to projective planes, *Trans. Amer. Math. Soc.* **65**, 473–474 (1949).
   Uniqueness of the projective plane with 57 points, *Proc. Amer. Math. Soc.* **4**, 912–916 (1953).
   Correction to above. *Proc. Amer. Math. Soc.* **5**, 994–997 (1954).
9. HALL, M., Jnr. *The Theory of Groups* (New York, 1959).
10. HILBERT, D. *Grundlagen der Geometrie* (Leipzig, 1930).
11. HODGE, SIR WILLIAM and PEDOE, D. *Methods of Algebraic Geometry* (Vol. I, Cambridge, 1947).
12. PICKERT, G. *Projektive Ebenen* (Berlin, 1955).
13. SEGRE, B. *Lezioni di Geometria Moderna* (Bologna, 1948).
14. TARRY, G. Le problème de 36 officiers, *C.R. Assoc. France Avanc. Sci. Natur.* **2**, 170–203 (1901).

215

INDEX

217